Contents

Draw lines to match the same patterns.

Concept: Match objects by attribute (pattern).
Introduction: Cut squares from various types of wrapping paper and have the child match squares with the same pattern. Discuss ways in which some squares from different patterns are similar; for example, both might have a lot of red colors, or both might have stars in the pattern.

Draw lines to join the same patterns.

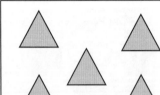
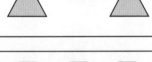
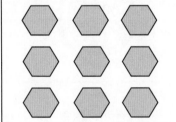

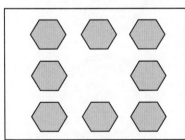

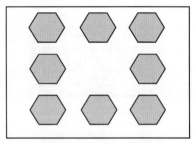
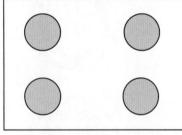
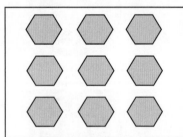
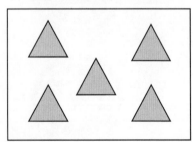

Concept: Match objects by attribute (pattern).
Introduction: Give some colored beads or counters to the child. Ask him/her to arrange the beads in a pattern.

Count and circle the correct number.

2   4   3

3   **1**   **4**

4   **2**   **1**

Concept: Count to four and recognize the numerals.
Introduction: Use blocks that link to each other. Have ready groups of 1, 2, 3, and 4 blocks. Ask the child to count the objects in a group and select the correct numeral card.

Color the correct number of birds in each row.

2

4

1

3

4

Concept: Count to four and recognize the numerals.
Introduction: Use blocks that link to each other. Hold up a numeral card and have the child link the correct number of blocks.
One Step Further: Give the child up to four counters or other small objects and have him/her guess the quantity before counting.

Count and draw a line to the correct number.

2

3

4

5

Concept: Count to five and recognize the numeral 5.

Introduction: Count out loud as you place four objects on the table: **one, two, three, four**. Pause and then tell the child that you are going to add one more. Place another object on the table, saying **five**. Count the objects on the table again. Ask the child how many objects there are. Show him/her the numeral card for 5. Tell the child that this is how we write the number 'five'. Remove objects from the table. Place three, four, or five objects on the table and have the child select the correct numeral card. Repeat.

Count and circle the correct number.

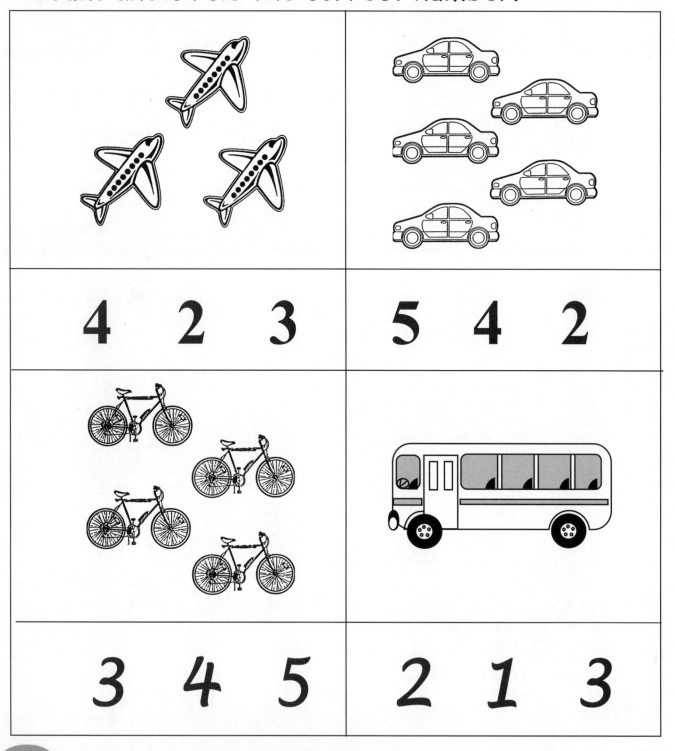

Concept: Count to five and recognize the numerals.
Introduction: Hold up five fingers and ask the child how many fingers he/she sees. Hold up the numeral cards for 1, 2, 3, 4, or 5 and ask the child to show you the number with his/her fingers.
One Step Further: Give the child some counters or other small object (up to five) and have him/her her guess the quantity before counting.

Draw the correct number of balls  in each box.

5	
3	
2	
4	

Concept: Count to five and recognize the numerals.
Introduction: Give the child verbal instructions on drawing a picture, e.g., draw a picture with 3 children and 2 dogs.
One Step Further: Have the child draw pictures with one, two, three, four, and five objects. For example, the child could draw a picture with one sun, two trees, three clouds, four flowers, and five rabbits. Do not insist that each number is represented. Have the child describe his/her picture, telling how many of each item has been drawn.

Circle groups of 5.

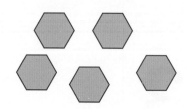

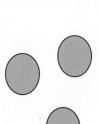

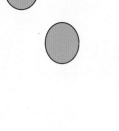

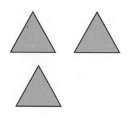

Concept: Recognize the number of objects in a group.
Introduction: Set out 1 to 5 counters on the table in a group, and see if the child can tell you how many there are without counting first. Repeat with other sets of 1-5 objects.

Color the correct number of blocks, starting with the block on the bottom.

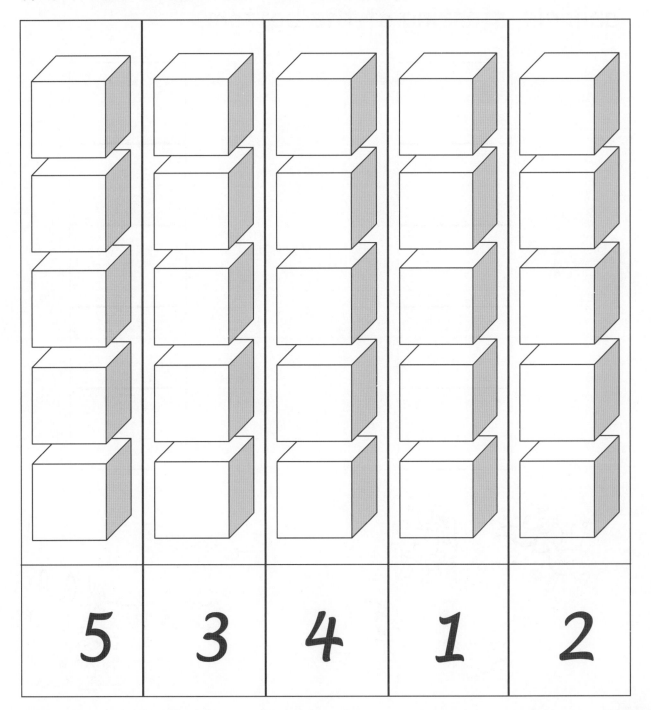

Concept: Introduce graphical representation of quantities.

Introduction: Use cubes that link or blocks that stack. Have 1 of one color, 2 of another color, 3 of a third color, 4 of a fourth color, and 5 of a fifth color (if available). Ask your child to make stacks of the blocks for each color and then tell you the number of blocks in each stack.

Using This Page: Guide the child in coloring the correct number by starting at the bottom of the stack, as if he/she were adding blocks to a stack.

Count the animals. Then color the correct number of boxes to show the number of animals, starting at the bottom.

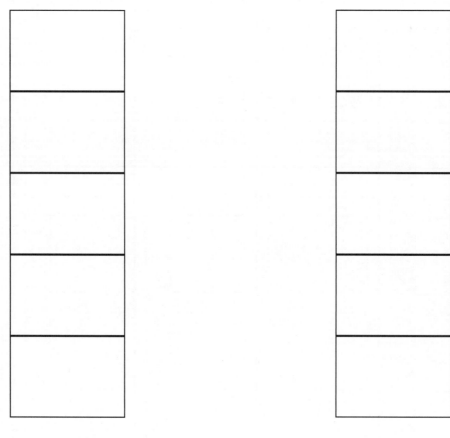

Concept: Use graphs as a way to tally objects.
Introduction: Display three sets of 1-5 objects. Each set should have the same type of objects. Have available cubes that link together. Assign a color to each set of objects. Have the child pair one object with one cube of the correct color for that set. Then have the child link the cubes for each color together and compare the stacks. Have him/her count the objects in each set and the number of cubes for that set to see that they are the same.

Count the clothes. Then color the correct number of boxes.

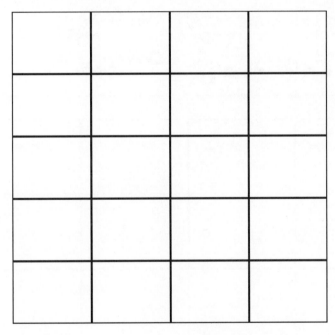

Concept: Use graphs as a way to tally objects.
Introduction: Display four sets of 1-5 objects. Each set should have the same type of objects. Draw a graph on the board consisting of an array of squares with 5 rows and 4 columns. Draw a picture at the bottom of each column representing each type of object. Guide the child in counting the objects and coloring the corresponding number of squares on the graph, starting with the bottom square.

Count the butterflies, ants, bees, and flowers in the park. Then color the boxes.

Concept: Use graphs as a way to tally objects.
Introduction: Use 4 colors of linking cubes. Have the child count the number in each set on this page (bees, butterflies, ants, and flowers), and the same number of cubes, a different color for each set. Have the child arrange the cubes next to each other in rows (rather than columns).
Using This Page: Guide the child in coloring the boxes starting at the left.
One Step Further: Ask the child questions such as: "Are there as many flowers as there are birds? Are there more ants than bees? Look at the boxes on the graph to tell me how many ants there are."

Count the dots. Draw the same number of dots in two different ways.

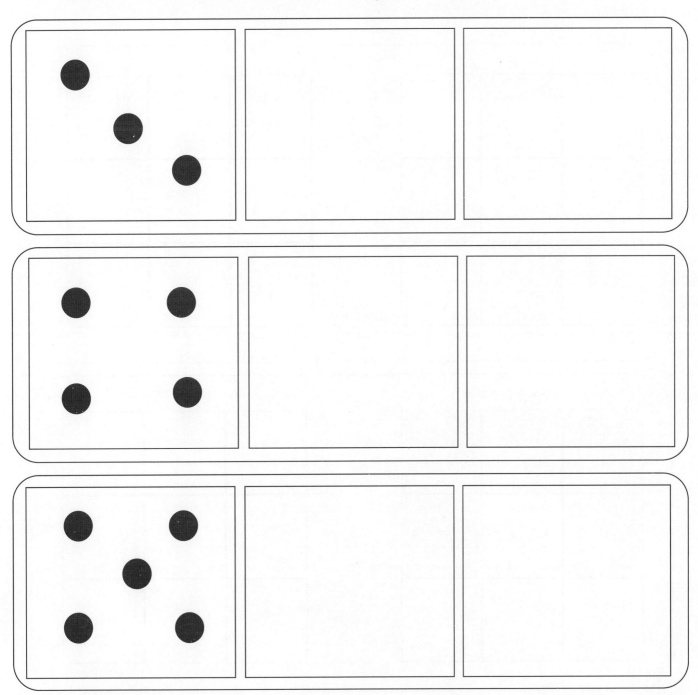

Concept: Understand the relationship between numbers and quantities.
Introduction: Put 5 crackers each on two identical plates. Put the crackers close together on one plate and spread them out on the other plate. Ask the child which plate of crackers he/she would like to have, and why. Have the child count the number of crackers on each plate and see that there is the same number. Move them around on the plate and ask if there is still the same number.

Count the colored boxes. Color the same number of boxes in a different pattern.

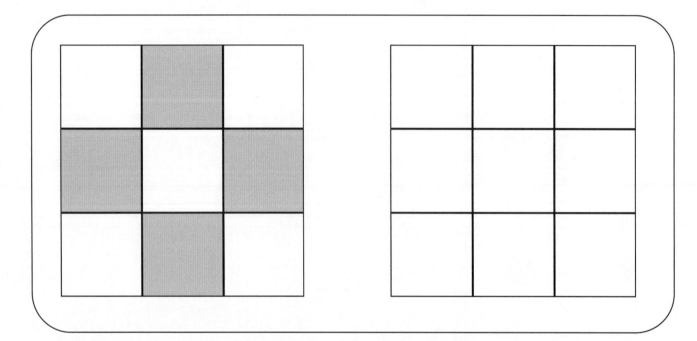

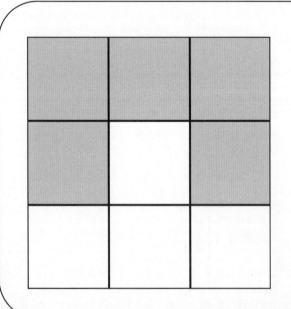

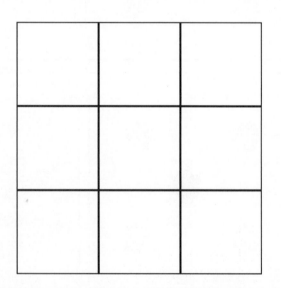

Concept: Understand the relationship between numbers and quantities.
Introduction: Use multilink cubes. Have the child count out 5 of each color. Then have him/her put each set together in a different way. Ask him/her if all the sets have the same number.

How many trees are on the beach? Follow the path to write 1s. Write some more 1s.

Concept: Write the numeral 1.
Introduction: Hold up one object or place one object on the table and ask the child, "How many___ are there?" Write the numeral 1 on the board. Tell the child that he/she will now learn to write '1'. Tell the child that in books, 1 is sometimes shown with a little extra bit near the top (1) and sometimes with a little line on the bottom (1). Write both versions on the board. Tell him/her we can write 1 as a straight line, starting at the top. Demonstrate. Have the child write a 1 in the air and on the board. Give additional opportunities to practice writing numerals.

How many crabs are on the beach? Follow the path to write 2s. Write some more 2s.

Concept: Write the numeral 2.
Introduction: Place one object on the table and ask the child how many there are. Add another object, and ask the child how many there are now. Write the numeral 2 on the board. Tell the child that he/she will learn to write the number 2. Demonstrate on the board. Have the child practice writing the number 2 in the air, on the board, in sand, on a large sheet of paper, with finger paint, etc.

How many starfish are on the beach? Follow the path to write 3s. Write some more 3s.

Concept: Write the numeral 3.
Introduction: Review counting to 3. Show the child how to write the numeral 3, and have him/her practice on the board or large sheets of paper.
One Step Further: Have the child start a number book. Add a page to it for each new number. Have the child write the number with crayons or markers and draw pictures or paste stickers showing sets of the quantity. Continue to add pages as the child learns to write the numerals.

Write the correct number in each box.

Concept: Practice writing numerals 1-3.
Introduction: Provide the child with 3 sheets of paper. Write the numerals 1, 2 and 3 on the board. Have the child copy each numeral on the paper and draw the corresponding set of objects. Have him/ her decorate the rest of the paper with more of the written numerals, using different colors, glitter pens, etc.

How many butterflies are in the park? Follow the path to write 4s. Write some more 4s.

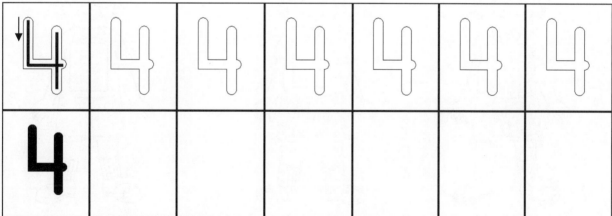

Concept: Write the numeral 4.
Introduction: Review counting to 4. Show the child how to write the numeral 4, and have him/her practice on the board or large sheets of paper. Tell the child that when we see '4' in books it looks different, with one side slanted to form a point with the other side, but we when we write it by hand, we come straight down instead. You can teach the child to say as he/she writes, "Down and over and down some more."

Trace a line to each boy. Write the number of toys he has on his shirt.

Concept: Practice writing numerals.
Introduction: Say a number 1 to 4 and ask the child to write it on the board. Repeat with another number. Draw a set of circles or stars on the board and ask the child to write the number. Repeat with another set of shapes.

How many bees are in the park? Follow the path to write 5s. Write some more 5s.

5	5	5	5	5	5	5
5						

Concept: Write the numeral 5.
Introduction: Review counting to 5. Show the child how to write the 5, and have him/her practice on the board or large sheets of paper. You can teach the child to say as he/she writes, "Down and around and give it a hat." Review writing other numerals as well.

Write the correct number in each box.

Concept: Practice writing numerals.
Introduction: Say a number 1 to 5 and ask the child to write it on the board. Repeat with another number.

Answer the questions below.

How many ? _____.

How many ? _____.

How many ? _____.

How many ? _____.

Concept: Interpret picture graphs.
Introduction: Look at the picture on this page. Tell the child that this is a picture graph that shows the number of insects seen at a park.
One Step Further: Aid the child in constructing a picture graph.

Answer the questions below.

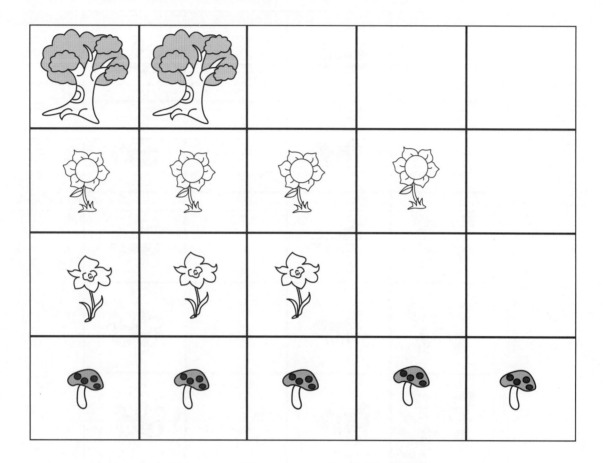

There were _____ .

There were _____ .

There were _____ .

There were _____ .

Concept: Interpret picture graphs.
Introduction: Look at the picture on this page. Tell the child that this is a picture graph that shows the number of plants a boy saw at a park.
One Step Further: Ask the child questions based on the graph, such as, "What did the boy see the most of?"

How many ants are in the park? Follow the path to write 6s. Write some more 6s.

6 6 6 6 6 6 6 6

6

Concept: Count to six and write the numeral 6.
Introduction: Count out loud as you place five objects on the table. Add one more object and tell the child that the next number after five is six. Have the child count the objects out loud along with you. Move the objects around and have the child count again. Write the numeral "6" on the board. Show the child how to write the numeral 6, and have him/her practice in the air, on the board, in sand, or on large sheets of paper using finger paints, crayon, or glue stick (add glitter). Review writing other numerals as well.

Count and circle the correct number.

⭐ ⭐ ⭐	**4** **5** **3**
🐟 🐟 🐟 🐟 🐟 🐟	**3** **6** **5**
🦆 🦆 🦆 🦆	**4** **2** **3**
🐿️ 🐿️ 🐿️ 🐿️ 🐿️ 🐿️	**2** **4** **6**

Concept: Count to six and recognize the numerals.
Introduction: Ask the child to throw a die, count the dots on the die, and pick out the same number of blocks or counters or other objects. Draw six objects on the board and show the child that as he/she counts he/she can mark each item just counted in order to know it has been counted already.

How many tails does this bug have? Follow the path to write 7s. Write some more 7s.

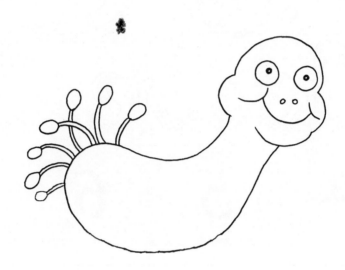

Concept: Count to seven and write the numeral 7.
Introduction: Introduce counting to 7 and reading and writing the numeral 7 using activities similar to those used for previous numerals. Provide opportunities for the child to count sets of up to 7 objects and to recognize the numerals 1-7. Give the child some counters and the numeral cards 1-7. Call out a number and have the child select the corresponding numeral card and set beside it the correct number of counters.

Count and circle the correct number.

4   5   6   7

6   1   3   7

Concept: Count to seven and recognize the numerals.
One Step Further: Teach the rhyme, "One potato, two potato, three potato, four. Five potato, six potato, seven potato, more." Have the child count potatoes as he/she says the rhyme, and clap when he/she says "more".

Write the correct number in each box.

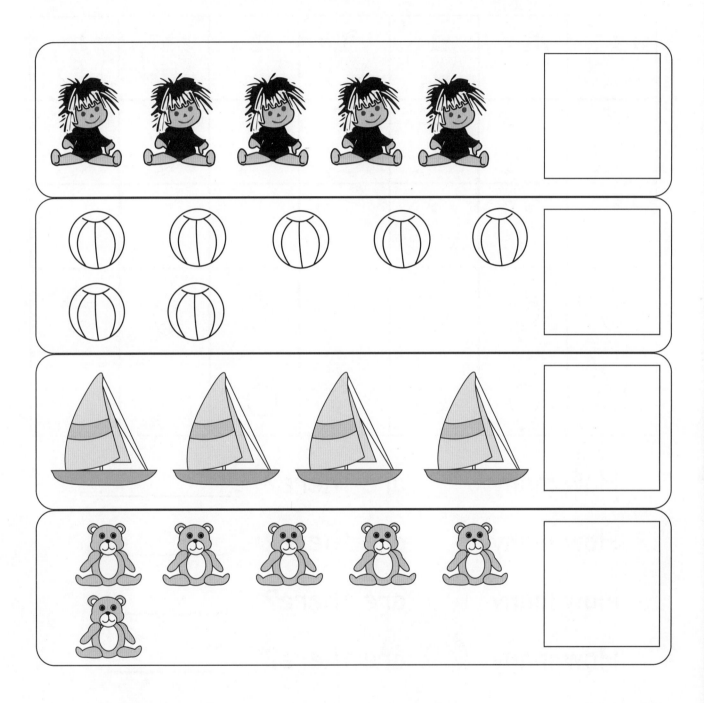

Concept: Practice writing numerals.
One Step Further: Give the child some counters or other small objects (up to 7) and have him/her her guess the quantity before counting.

Answer the questions below.

How many are there? _____.

How many are there? _____.

How many are there? _____.

How many are there? _____.

How many are there? _____.

Concept: Interpret picture graphs.
Introduction: Look at the picture on this page. Tell the child that this is a picture graph that shows the number of fruit in a fruit bowl.
One Step Further: Ask the child questions based on the graph, such as, "Were there more apples or oranges?"

How many spots does this bug have? Follow the path to write 8s. Write some more 8s.

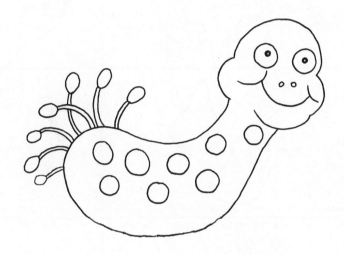

Concept: Count to eight and write the numeral 8.
Introduction: Introduce counting to 8 and the numeral 8 using activities similar to those used for previous numerals. Show the child how to write the 8, and have him/her practice on the board or large sheets of paper. If the child has been learning to write "S" you can tell him/her to start the 8 like a S that keeps going back to the start. Review writing other numerals as well.

Count and circle the correct number.

(cherries)	6 7 8
(pears)	7 1 5
(bananas)	6 7 8
(strawberries)	8 3 6

Concept: Count to eight and recognize the numerals.

How many legs does this bug have? Follow the path to write 9s. Write some more 9s.

9 9 9 9 9 9 9

9

Concept: Count to nine and write the numeral 9.
Introduction: Introduce counting to 9 and the numeral 9 using activities similar to those used for previous numerals. Draw a 9 on the board as it is generally shown in books, and also as it is generally drawn, with a straight part. Tell the child that both are ways to write 9 and that in books the tail of the 9 is curves around more, but we don't have to curve it around when writing it.

Count and circle the correct number.

	6 9 8
	9 5 7
	9 7 1
	6 3 9

Concept: Count to nine and recognize the numerals.

How many balloons are there? Follow the path to write 10s. Write some more 10s.

Concept: Count to ten and write 10.
Introduction: Introduce counting to 10 and the numeral 10 using activities similar to those used for previous numerals. Hold up a numeral card, and ask the child to clap his/her hands while you count. Then you clap your hands while the child counts. Repeat with other numbers and actions, such as hopping on one foot, jumping in place, or patting the top of his/her own head.

Count and circle the correct number.

(hammers)	**8 9 10**
(nails)	**10 5 7**
(pliers)	**6 9 4**
(nuts)	**9 10 1**

Concept: Count to ten and recognize the numerals.
One Step Further: Teach the child some number rhymes, such as, "One, two, buckle my shoe, three four, shut the door, five, six, pick up sticks, seven eight, lay them straight, nine, ten, a big, fat hen." and, "One, two, three, four, five, once I caught a fish alive. Six, seven, eight, nine, ten, then I let it go again."

Draw 7 spots on the dinosaur.

Draw 10 spots on the ladybug.

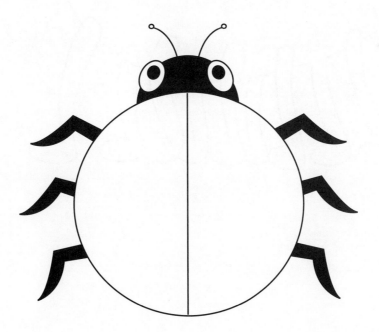

Concept: Practice counting.
One Step Further: Have the child draw cards from a deck containing the cards 2-10 and name the numeral. Give the child a handful of counters, up to 10, and have him/her estimate the number, then count.

Draw 10 spots, 5 tails, and 2 eyes on the bug.

Concept: Practice counting.
One Step Further: Have the child draw a picture and talk about how many of certain items there are in the picture. Have the child look at posters or other pictures and talk about the number of certain items there are in the picture. Have the child draw his/her own "bugs" and count the parts.

Write the correct number in each box.

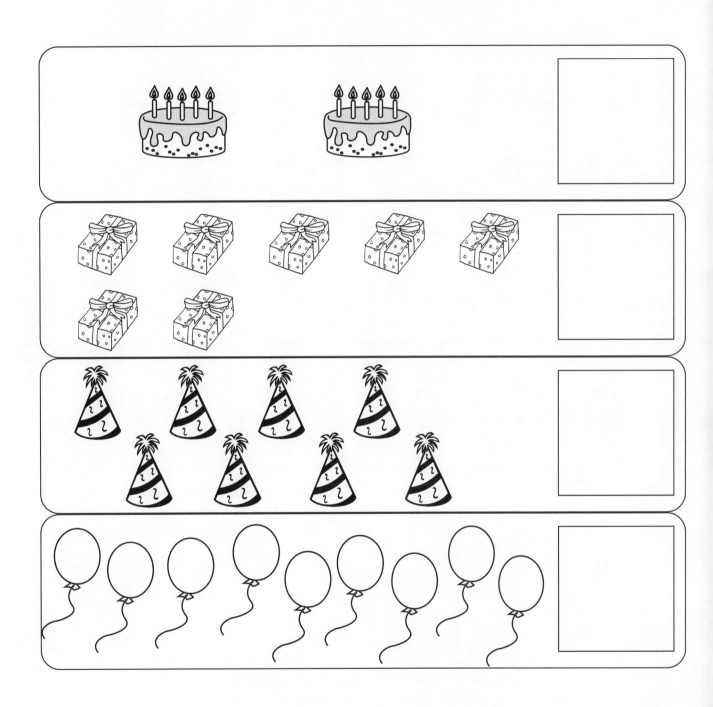

Concept: Practice counting and writing numerals.
Introduction: Call out numbers between 1 and 9 and have the child write them on the board.

Write the correct number in each box.

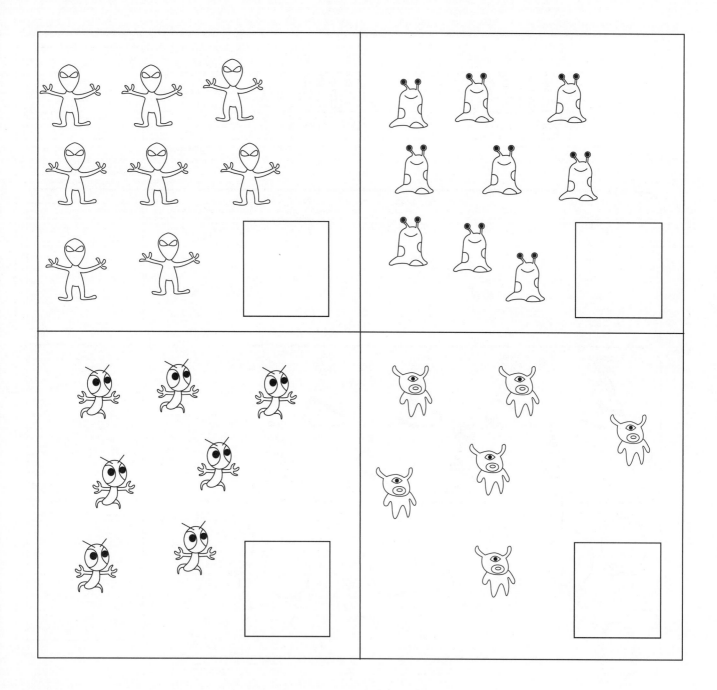

Concept: Count and write numerals.
Introduction: Call out numbers between 1 and 9 and have the child write them on the board.

How many coconuts are still on the tree? Follow the path to write 0s. Write some more 0s.

Concept: Understand the concept of the empty set and write 0.
Introduction: Display 5 plastic pins or balls on the table. Ask a child how many there are. Knock one off and ask again how many there are. Continue until the last one is knocked off. Tell the child that 'zero' stands for none, or nothing. Show a number card for '0' and write 0 on the board. Have the child practice writing 0.

Count and write the correct number.

Concept: Understand the concept of the empty set.
Introduction: Teach the child the rhyme "Five little monkeys jumping on the bed. One fell off and bumped his head. Mama called the doctor and the doctor said, 'No more monkeys jumping on the bed!' Four little monkeys jumping on the bed…" and so on, ending with "No little monkeys jumping on the bed." Write the number of monkeys at the start of each verse. When there are no monkeys left, write "0" and remind them that '0' means 'zero' which is the same as 'none'. The child can act out the rhyme, starting with up to 10 monkeys on the bed.

Fill in the correct numbers.

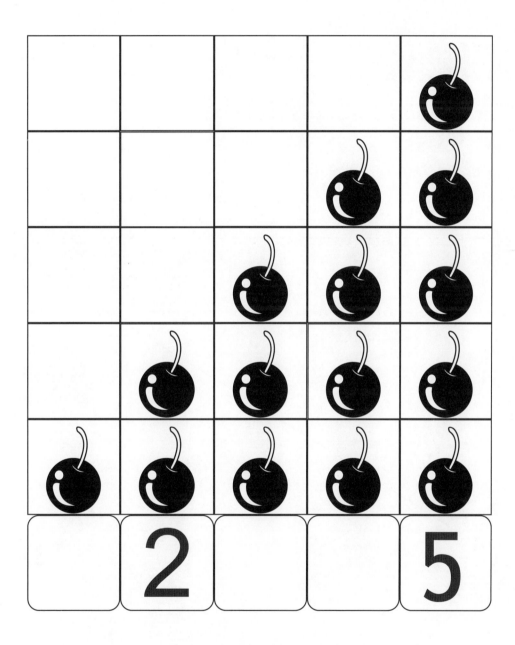

Concept: Understand that numbers have order.
Introduction: Have the child make towers of blocks or linking cubes, with one, two, three, four, and five blocks. Have him/her put them in order. Draw similar squares or blocks on the board in a step-pattern. Point to the first tower and ask how many blocks are in it. Write the number 1 under the tower. Tell the child that the next tower has one more block and ask him/her how many blocks are in it. Write the number 2 under the tower. Tell the child that 2 is more than 1. Continue through 5.

Join the dots in order from 1 to 5 to make a star.

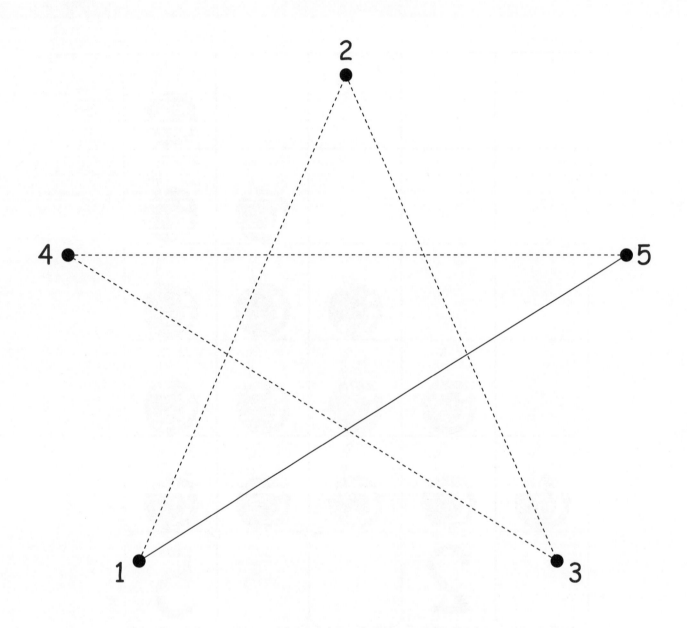

Concept: Understand that numbers have order.
Introduction: Give the child a set of number cards 1-5 and have him/her arrange the cards in order. Ask questions such as, "What number comes after 2?"
One Step Further: The child may like drawing 5-pointed stars on his/her own.

Fill in the missing numbers.

| 1 | | | | 5 | | | | | 10 |

Concept: Understand that numbers have order.
Introduction: Have the child make towers of blocks or linking cubes, with one through ten blocks. Have him/her put them in order. Point to the first tower and ask how many blocks are in it. Place the numeral card 1 under the tower. Tell the child that the next tower has one more block and ask him/her how many blocks are in it. Place the numeral card 2 under the tower. Tell the child that 2 is more than 1. Continue through 10.

Join the dots from 1 to 10 to complete this picture.

1 .

2 .

3 .

4 .

5 .

6 .

. 10

. 9

. 8

. 7

Concept: Understand that numbers have order.
Introduction: Display the numeral cards 1-10 in random order. Have the child put them in order. Ask the child questions like, "What comes after 3?" Reinforce the idea that the order is fixed, e.g. 6 always comes after 5.

Fill in the missing numbers.

Concept: Understand that number order does not change even if some numbers are missing.
Introduction: Display the numeral cards 1-5 in order. Ask the child to read the numbers. Remove a number and ask the child for the missing number. Repeat with a different number. Repeat, removing several numbers.

Write the missing numbers to count the bees.

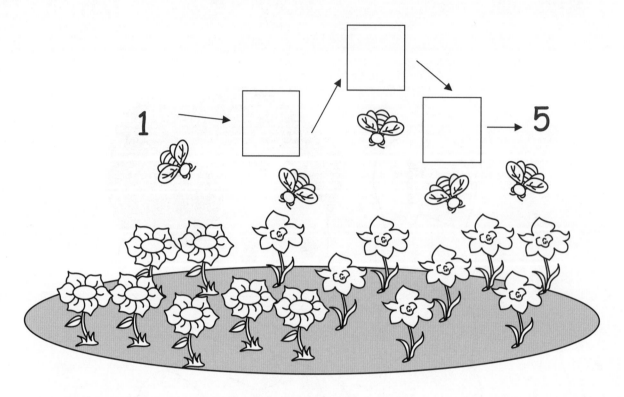

1 → ☐ → ☐ → ☐ → 5

Fill in the missing numbers.

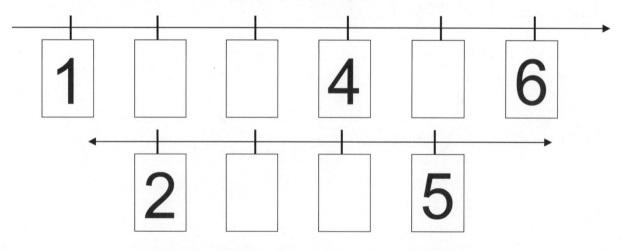

1 ☐ ☐ 4 ☐ 6

☐ 2 ☐ ☐ 5

Concept: Understand that number order does not change even if some numbers are missing.

Draw dots in the empty card to finish the pattern. Fill in the missing numbers.

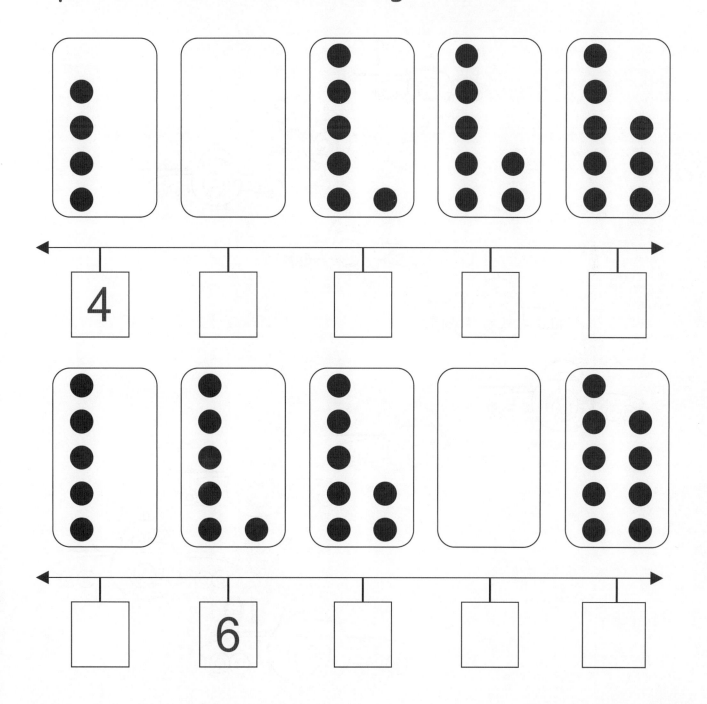

Concept: Understand that number order does not change even if some numbers are missing.
Introduction: Display the numeral cards 1-10 in order. Ask the child to read the numbers. Remove all but five consecutive cards. Then remove one or more cards between the first and last of the consecutive cards. Show the cards that have been removed and ask the child where to put them between the remaining two cards.

Fill in the missing numbers.

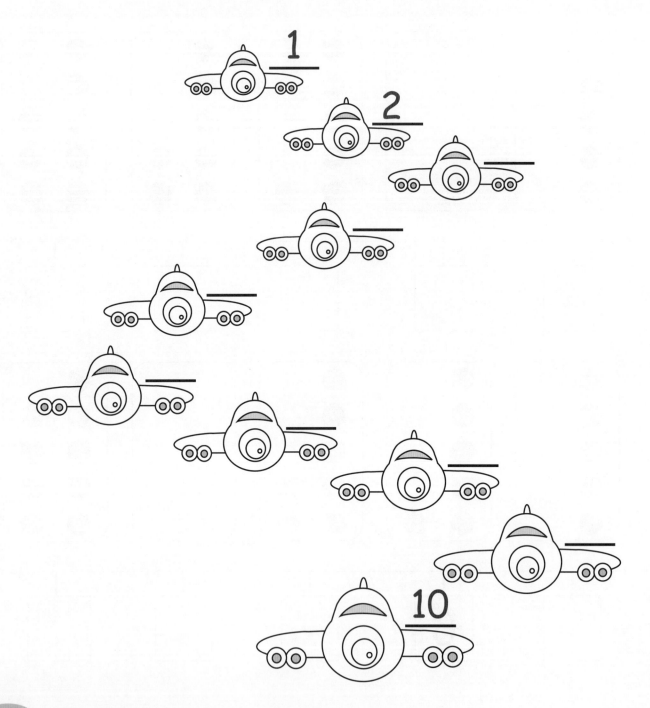

Concept: Understand that numbers have order.
Introduction: Ask the child to write the numbers 1-10 in order.

Fill in the missing numbers.

Concept: Understand that numbers have order.
Introduction: Display only the first and last of a set of consecutive numbers. Give the child the numbers that go in between and ask him or her to put them in order between the two numbers.
One Step Further: Display the number cards 1-10 in order. Point to 7, then point to the number before it. Tell the child, "Six comes before seven." Ask the child what number comes before and after another number.

Fill in the missing numbers.

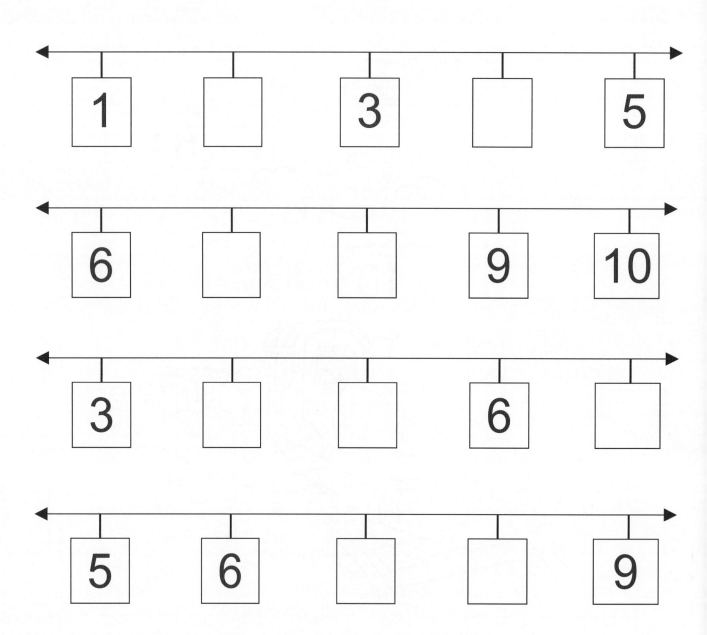

1 ☐ 3 ☐ 5

6 ☐ ☐ 9 10

3 ☐ ☐ 6 ☐

5 6 ☐ ☐ 9

Concept: Understand that number order does not change even if some numbers are missing.
Introduction: Draw 10 items on the board and number the first four of them 1-4 as the child counts them for you. Erase the first three, along with their numbers. Tell the child you have already counted the first three, so now you are at 4. The next one is 5. Continue counting and writing the numbers to 10. Erase the last 2, and the numbers in between 4 and 8. Ask the child what numbers are needed to fill in the numbers between 4 and 8 again.

Color the squares and fill in the missing numbers.

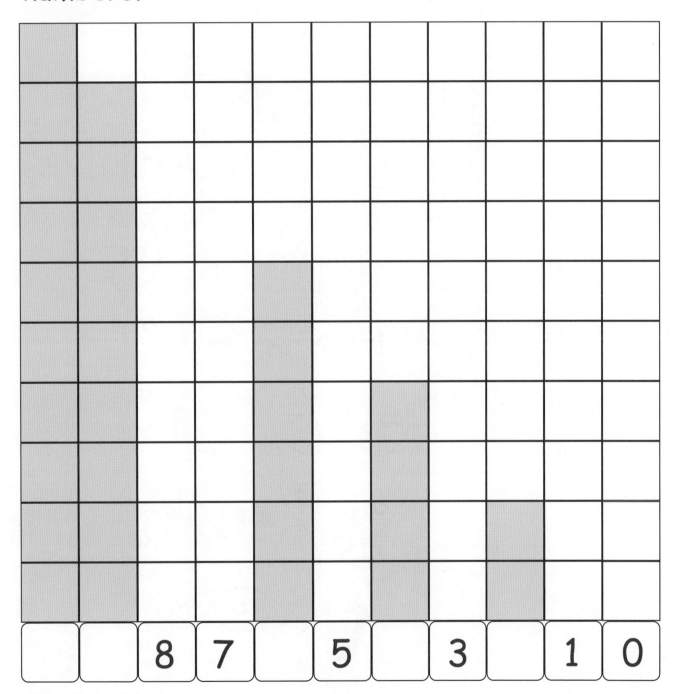

| | | 8 | 7 | | 5 | | 3 | | 1 | 0 |

Concept: Understand that numbers can have reverse order.
Introduction: Have the child make towers of blocks or linking cubes, with one through ten blocks. Put the numeral cards 10 to 1 in descending order in a row. Have the child match a tower with each number. Tell the child that the numbers are now in backwards, or count-down, order. Have the child count down from 10 to 0.

Help Piggy find his way back home. Color the stones from **10** to **1**.

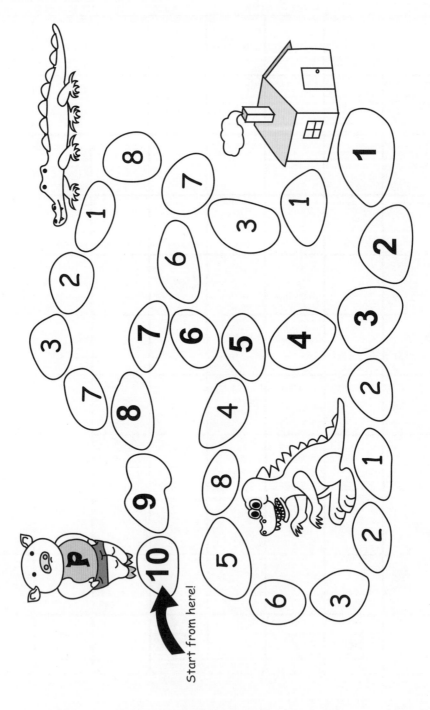

Start from here!

Concept: Understand that numbers can have reverse order.
Introduction: Give the child the numeral cards 10 to 0 and ask him/her to set out the 10 first and then the rest in count-down order.

Draw dots in the empty card to finish the pattern. Fill in the missing numbers.

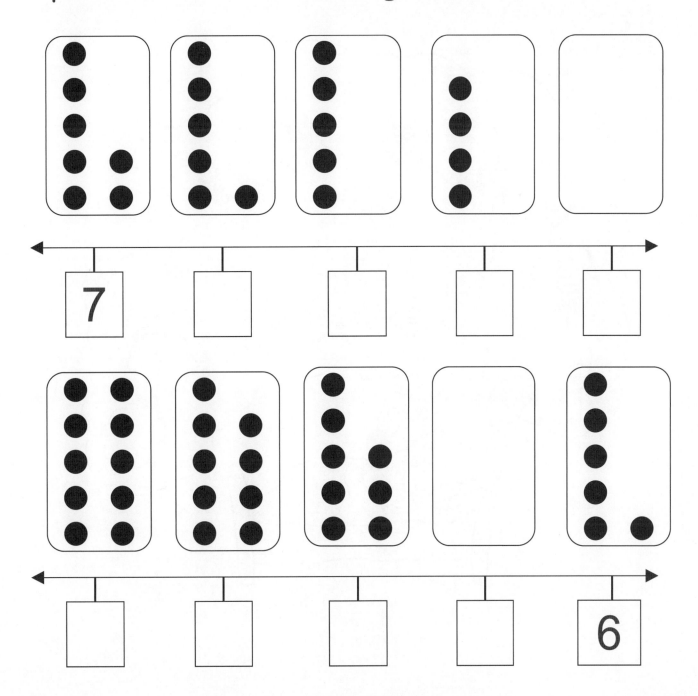

Concept: Understand that numbers have reverse order.
Introduction: Write the numbers 1-10 on the board, leaving some out. Ask the child to fill in the missing numbers.

Fill in the missing numbers.

Concept: Understand that numbers have order.
Introduction: Tell the child a story of a girl who was trying to go to sleep by counting backwards. Ask the child to write the numbers 10-1 in count-down order.

Fill in the missing numbers.

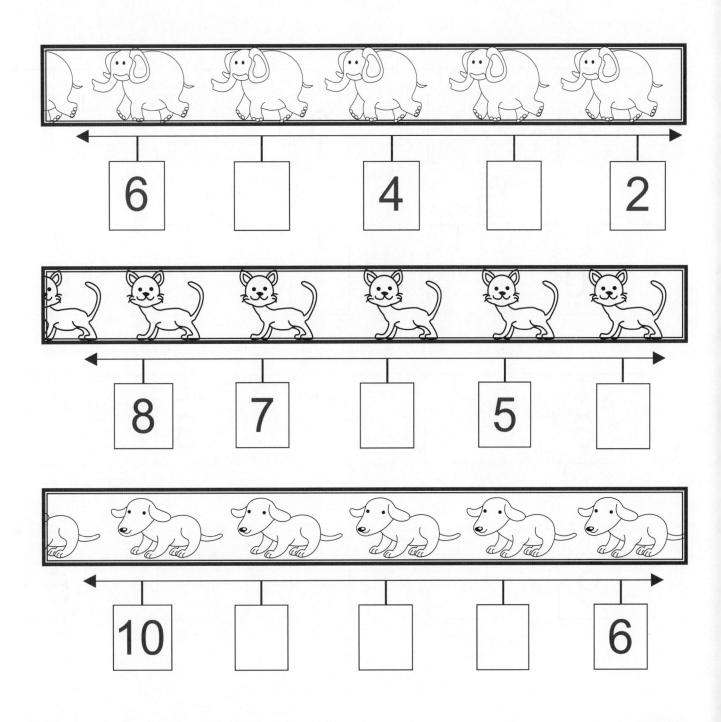

Concept: Understand that numbers have order.
Introduction: Set out 10 objects in a line. Have the child count them. Have one "walk away" and ask the child to tell you how many there are (without counting again). Continue, removing one object at a time.

Fill in the missing numbers.

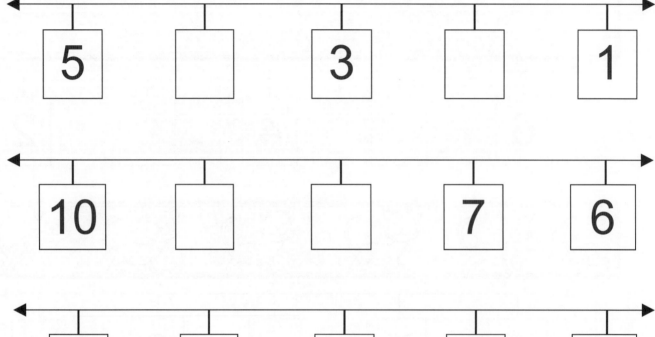

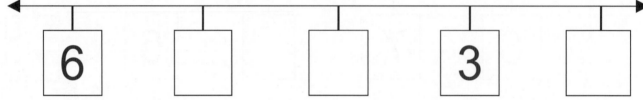

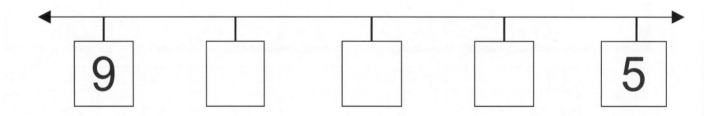

Concept: Understand that number order does not change even if some numbers are missing.
Introduction: Have the child put the numeral cards 10-1 in count-down order. Remove some, mix them up, and have the child replace them. Write two non-consecutive numbers on the board, with the larger number to the left, or set out two non-consecutive number cards. Get the child to fill in the missing numbers in count-down order.

Trace the shapes and color.

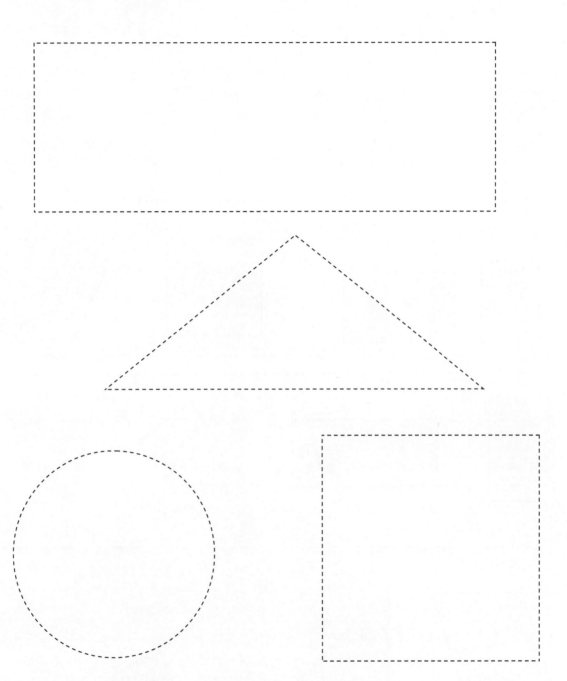

Concept: Identify and compare basic shapes.
Introduction: Have ready a variety of cut-outs of squares, circles, rectangles, and triangles. Let the child examine them. Discuss their similarities and differences and have the child sort them into groups. Help the child distinguish rectangles from squares, or group them together for now. Name the groups; e.g., "These are all circles."

Cross out the shape that does not belong.

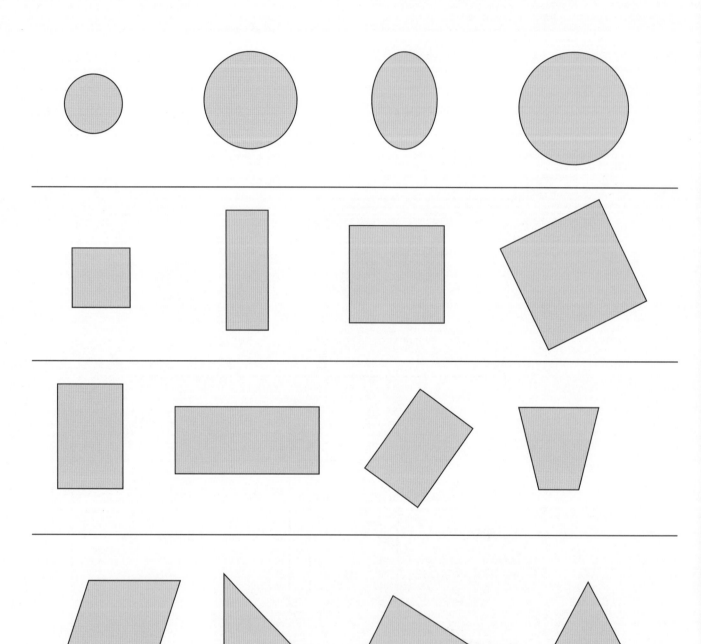

Concept: Sort by attribute (shape).

Trace the house. Add in windows and doors using the given shapes.

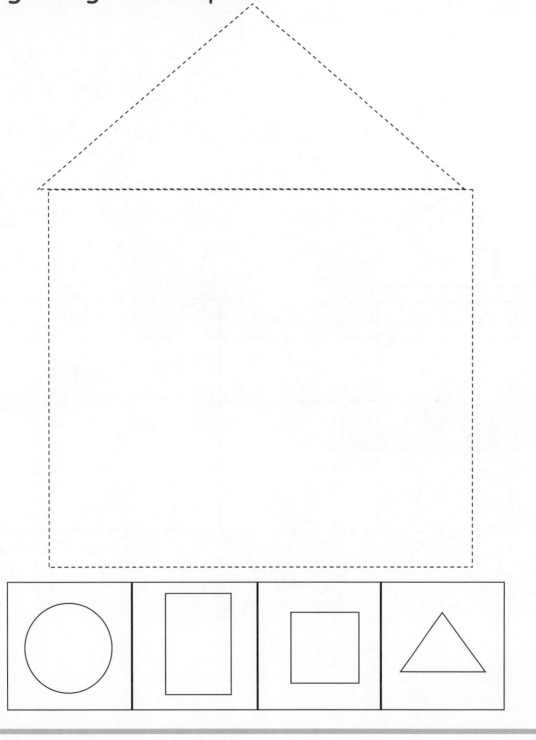

Concept: Identify and compare basic shapes.
One Step Further: Draw a square. Draw some straight lines in the square. Help the child see that a square can be made up of two triangles, etc.

Trace the shapes and color.

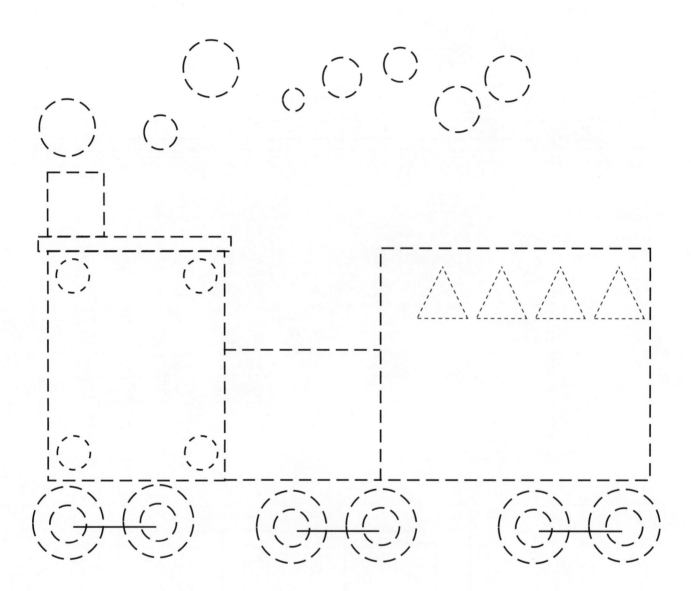

Concept: Identify and compare basic shapes.
One Step Further: Show the child some circles, rectangles, squares, and triangles. Talk about curved edges and straight edges. Point to the corners on the rectangles and identify them as corners. Get the child to count the number of straight edges and corners on the rectangles, squares, and triangles.

Count the shapes and fill in the blanks.

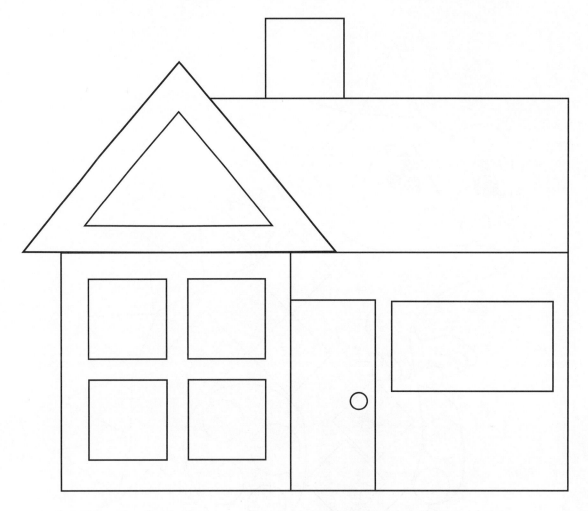

There are _____ squares ☐ .

There are _____ rectangles ▭ .

There are _____ triangles △ .

There are _____ circles ○ .

Concept: Identify and sort basic shapes.
Introduction: Use up to 10 cutouts of each shape. Ask the child to sort and count them.

Color the picture according to the chart.

△	red
○	yellow
◇	green

Concept: Identify and compare basic shapes.
Using This Page: Color the words in the chart before the child uses this page.
One Step Further: Have the child draw a picture containing the basic shapes.

Match the shapes.

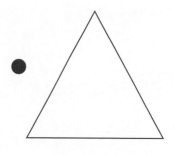

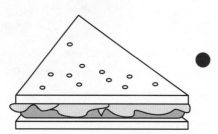

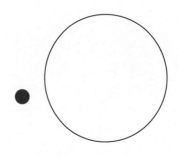

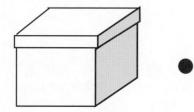

Concept: Identify basic shapes on solids.
Introduction: Ask the child to find common shapes on the surfaces or as parts of familiar objects; e.g. a circle for the rim of a cup. Identify the faces of various objects.

Draw a lines to match similar shapes.

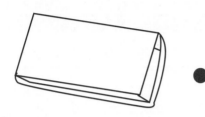   •   •   

   •   •   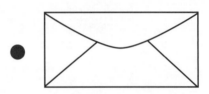

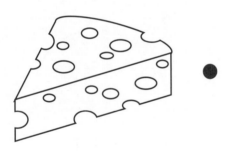   •   •   

   •   •   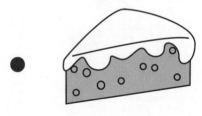

Concept: Match solids with similar basic shapes.
Introduction: Have various solid shapes with flat faces available. Guide the child in tracing around the faces to make shapes.
One Step Further: Have cubes, cylinders, boxes, and cones made from sponge or potato. Let the child use poster paint to make prints.

Draw lines to match.

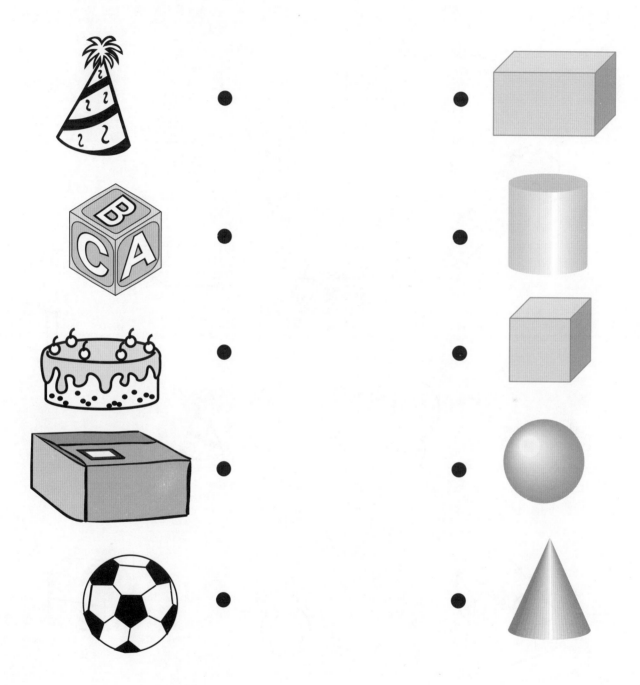

Concept: Recognize solid shapes.
Introduction: Provide a variety of solid shapes: cubes, boxes, spheres, cylinders, and cones. Have the child sort them by shape.

Circle objects that are shaped like cubes.

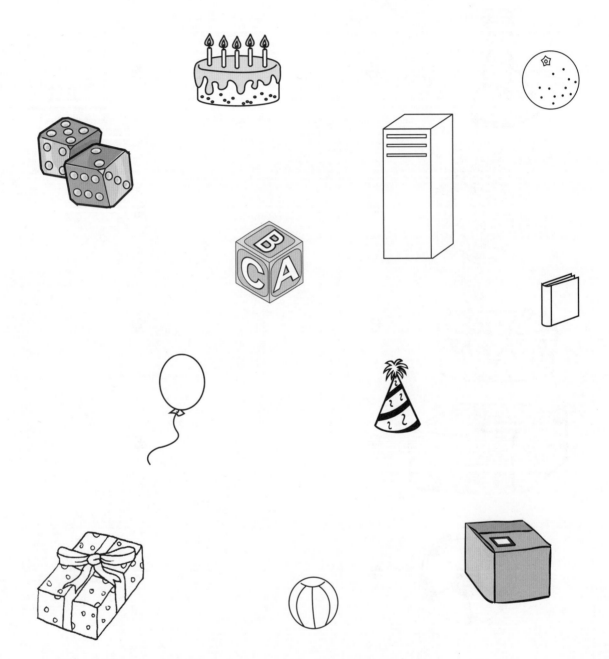

Concept: Recognize solid shapes.
Introduction: Provide a variety of objects in the shape of a cubes and boxes, as well as other solid shapes. Hold up a cube and say, "This is a cube." Have the child repeat the name. Show the child that all the faces are shaped like squares and are the same. Help the child count the faces and corners. Ask the child to find other objects that have the shape of a cube. Also have him/her find an objects where a part is shaped like a cube. Compare the cube to a box shape. A box is not a cube because the sides are not all squares.

Circle objects that are shaped like boxes.

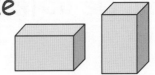

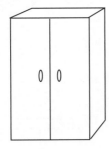

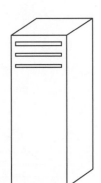

Concept: Recognize solid shapes.
Introduction: Provide a variety of objects in the shape of a cubes and boxes, as well as other solid shapes. Hold up a box and say, "This is shaped like a box." Have the child count the faces and corners. Ask them how it is different from a cube. Ask the child to find other objects that have the shape of a box.

Circle objects that are shaped like spheres.

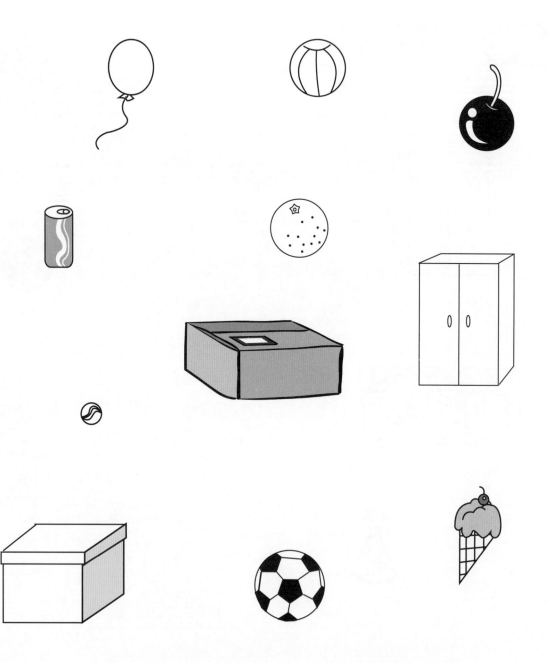

Concept: Recognize solid shapes.

Introduction: Provide a variety of solid shapes, including a number of spheres. Hold up a sphere and say, "This is a sphere." Have the child repeat the name. Tell him/her that most balls are shaped like spheres. If you have eggs or other oval solid, show it to the child and ask if it is a sphere. Ask the child to find other objects that have the shape of a sphere.

One Step Further: Put some box and sphere shaped objects into paper or cloth bags, or hide them under a cloth. Ask the child to feel the shapes without looking and select the spheres.

Circle objects that are shaped like cylinders.

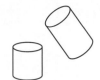

Concept: Recognize solid shapes.
Introduction: Provide a variety of solid shapes, including a number of cylinders. Hold up a cylinder and say, "This is a cylinder." Have the child repeat the name. Show him/her a can and tell the child that most cans are shaped like cylinders. Show him/her something that is not a can, such as a candle, but is shaped like a cylinder. Ask the child to find other objects that have the shape of a cylinder. Review the names of a cube, a box, and a sphere.

Circle objects that are shaped like cones.

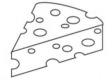

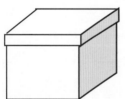

Concept: Recognize solid shapes.
Introduction: Provide a variety of solid shapes, including a number of cones. Hold up a cone and say, "This is a cone." Have the child repeat the name. Show the child a cylinder and ask how a cone is different from a cylinder. Ask the child to find other objects or parts of objects that have the shape of a cylinder. Review the names of the other shapes already learned.
Extension: Put some small objects of different shapes into paper or cloth bags, or hide them under a cloth. Ask the child to feel the shape without looking at it and tell you its name.

Look at the pattern below. Color the unshaded parts.

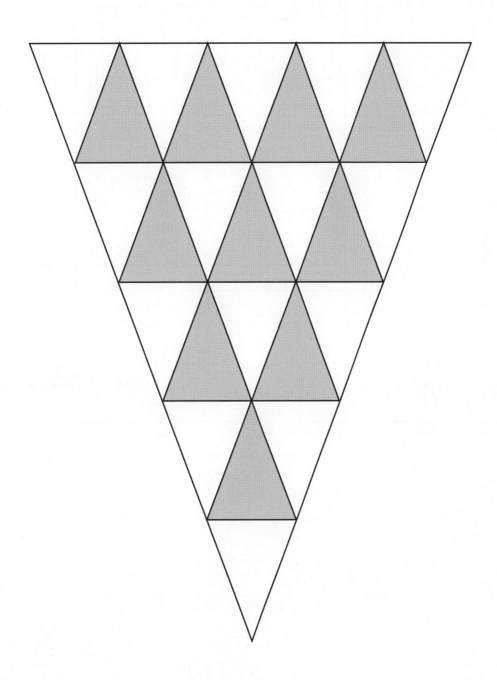

Concept: Shapes can be used to make patterns.
Introduction: Point out and talk about regular patterns; e.g., in clothing, in the tiles on floors.

Look at the pattern below. Color the small squares.

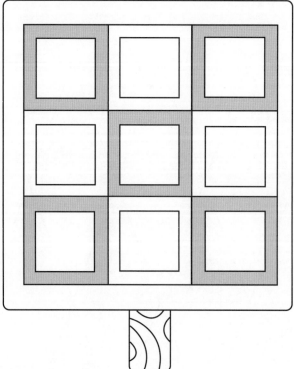

Make your own pattern.

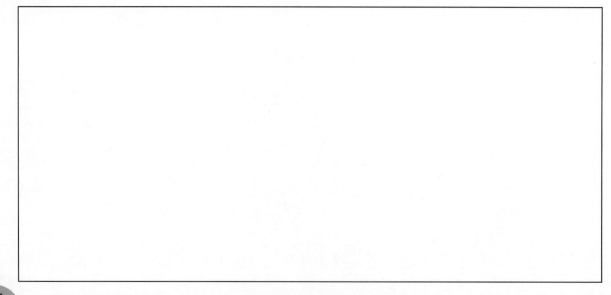

Concept: Shapes can be used to make patterns.
One Step Further: Encourage the child to talk about regular patterns that he/she sees around the home or school. Ask the child what makes the pattern regular.

Circle the picture that comes next in the pattern.

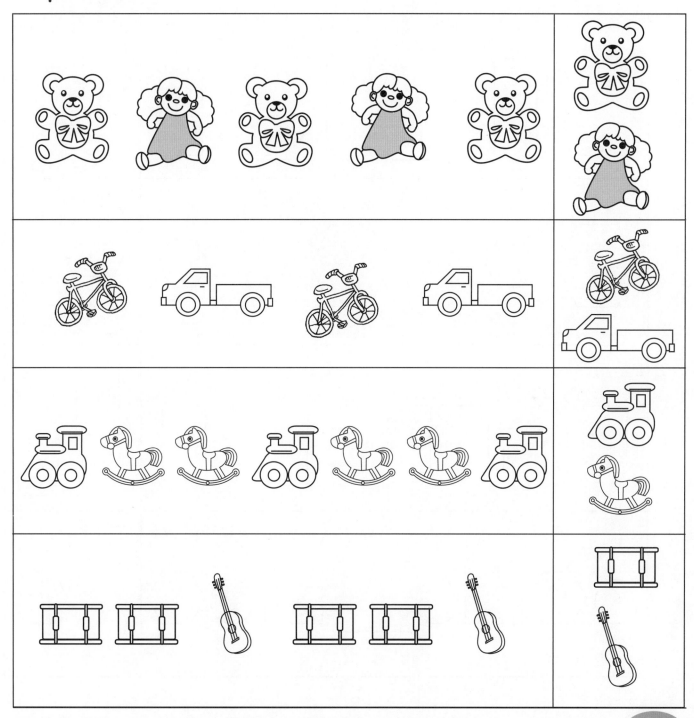

Concept: Identify, describe, and extend simple patterns.
Introduction: Arrange two different objects to form a pattern that repeats itself every two objects. Tell the child to describe the pattern by saying the names of the objects; e.g. "ball, block, ball, block, ball, block…" Ask the child what would come next to continue the pattern. Tell the child that the pattern repeats every two objects. Repeat with a pattern that repeat every three objects, e.g., ball, ball, block, ball, ball, block.

Patterns

Color the shape that is missing in each pattern.

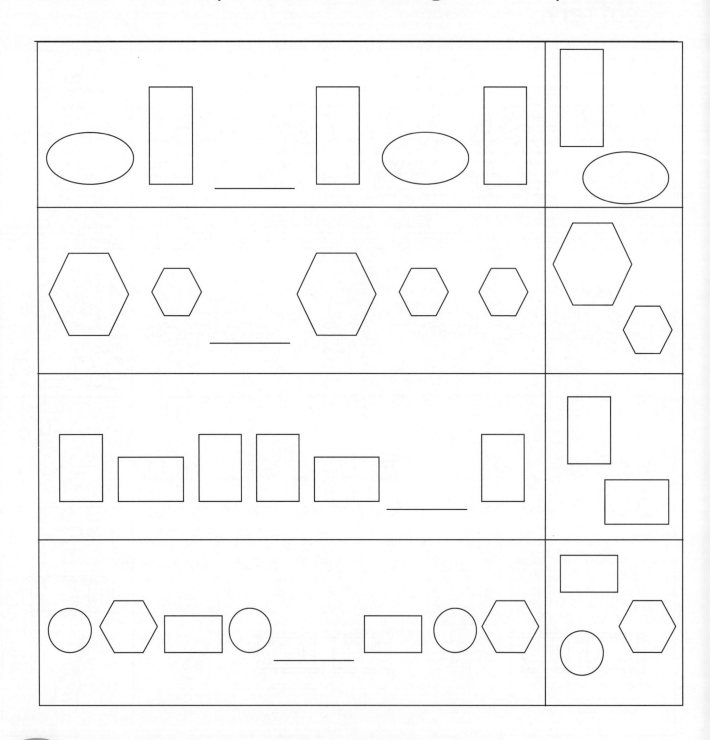

Concept: Identify, describe, and extend simple patterns.
Introduction: Arrange two different objects to form a pattern that repeats itself every three objects, with an object missing. Ask the child what object would be needed to complete the pattern.
One Step Further: Let the child create patterns with beads on a string to make a necklace.

Color the blocks to make a pattern.

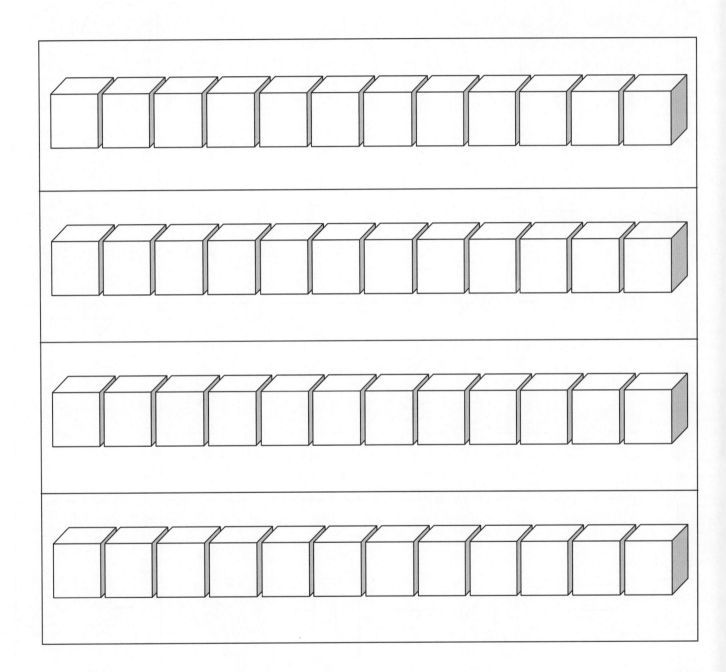

Concept: Identify, describe, and extend simple patterns.
Introduction: Use linking cubes to create a pattern based on color. Get the child to identify the pattern. Ask the child to make another pattern based on color.

Color the shape that comes next in the pattern.

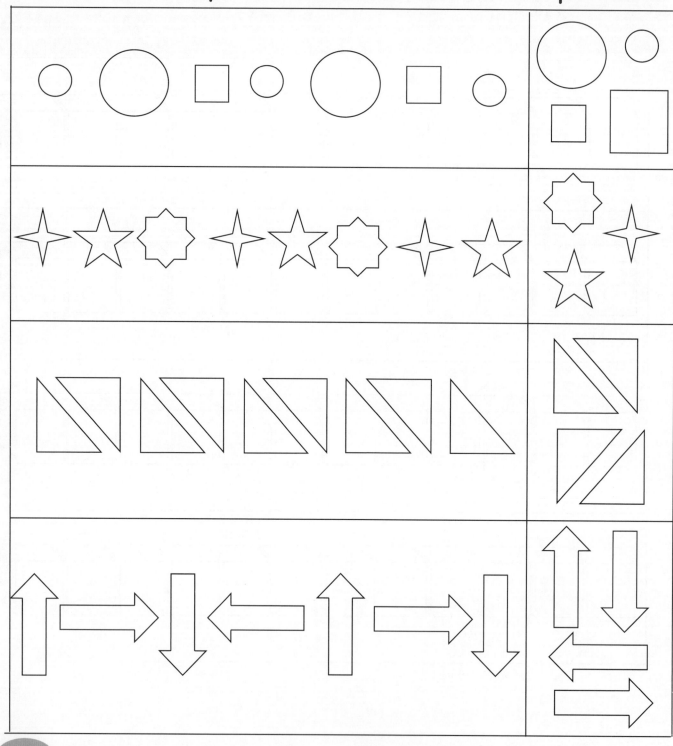

Concept: Identify, describe, and extend simple patterns.
Introduction: Arrange three types of objects or shapes to form a pattern that repeats itself every three or four objects. The pattern can be the orientation of a shape. Tell the child to describe the pattern with words; e.g. "up, this way, down, that way,…" Ask the child what would come next to continue the pattern.
One Step Further: Have the child circle the repeating groups on this page.

Trace to complete the following patterns.

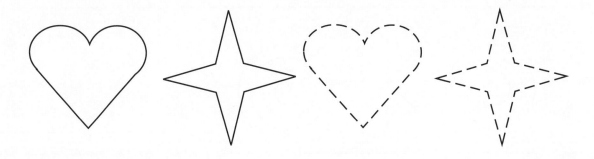

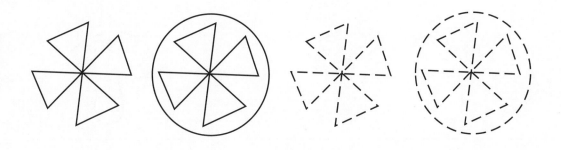

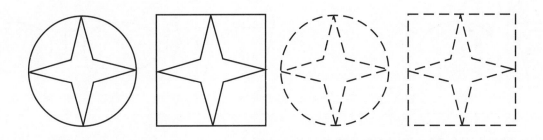

Concept: Identify, describe, and extend simple patterns.
One Step Further: Provide the child with cutout shapes or other sets of objects and ask him/her to create a simple pattern made from combinations of shapes.

Draw to complete the following patterns.

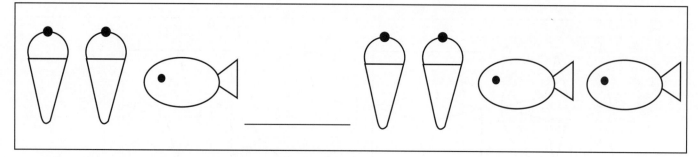

Make your own pattern.

Concept: Identify, describe, and extend simple patterns.
One Step Further: Help the child make a greeting card with a pattern around the edges of the card.

Fill in the blanks.

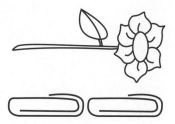

This flower is ____ paper-clips long.

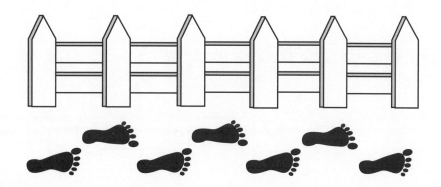

This fence is ____ footsteps long.

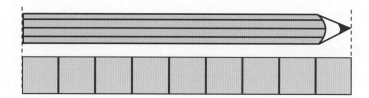

This pencil is ____ squares long.

Concept: Compare the length of objects by making direct comparison with reference objects.
Introduction: Get the child to measure the lengths of different objects with paper clips, blocks, craft sticks, etc.
One Step Further: Get the child to measure and compare distances between furniture or other objects in the room, the length and width of various rooms, using paces or footsteps.

Guess, and then measure with blocks.

Guess: _____ long

Measure: _____ long

Guess: _____ long

Measure: _____ long

Guess: _____ long

Measure: _____ long

Concept: Compare the length of objects by making direct comparison with reference objects.
Introduction: Provide various objects to measure and various items to measure with, such as paper-clips, centimeter cubes, craft sticks, etc. Ask the child to first estimate the lengths or heights, and then measure. The items should not measure more than 10 of the measuring units.
Using This Page: Provide the child with centimeter cubes to measure with.

How long are the objects? Write your answers in the rectangles.

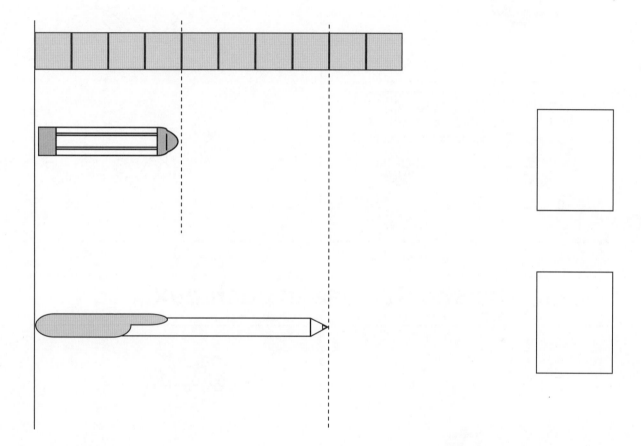

Circle the object that is shorter.
Color the object that is longer.

Concept: Compare the length of objects.
Introduction: Display a set of long and short objects. Ask the child to select two objects and tell you which one is shorter than the other, or which one is longer than the other. Name pairs of objects in the room and discuss with the child which is short and which is long. Encourage the child to point to long and short objects around him/her. Point to two objects that are similar in length. Ask the child how we can compare them if we cannot move them. We can measure them with another object, such as linking blocks, or string, and then bring the blocks or string next to the other object.

Circle the longer one in each box.

Circle the shorter one in each box.

Concept: Compare the length of objects.
One Step Further: After the child has finished this page, discuss which object in each set is longer than or shorter than the other, using the language 'longer than' or 'shorter than'. For example, the screwdriver is longer than the wrench.

How long are the objects? Write your answers in the rectangles.

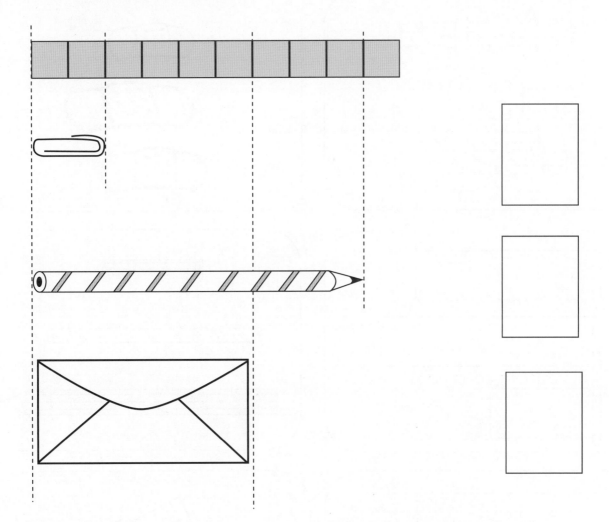

Circle the object that is shortest.
Color the object that is longest.

Concept: Compare the length of objects.
Introduction: Give the child three lengths of straw. Have the child tell you which one is longest, and which one is shortest. Point out several objects in the room, and ask the child which is longest or shortest.

Circle the longest one. Cross off the shortest one.

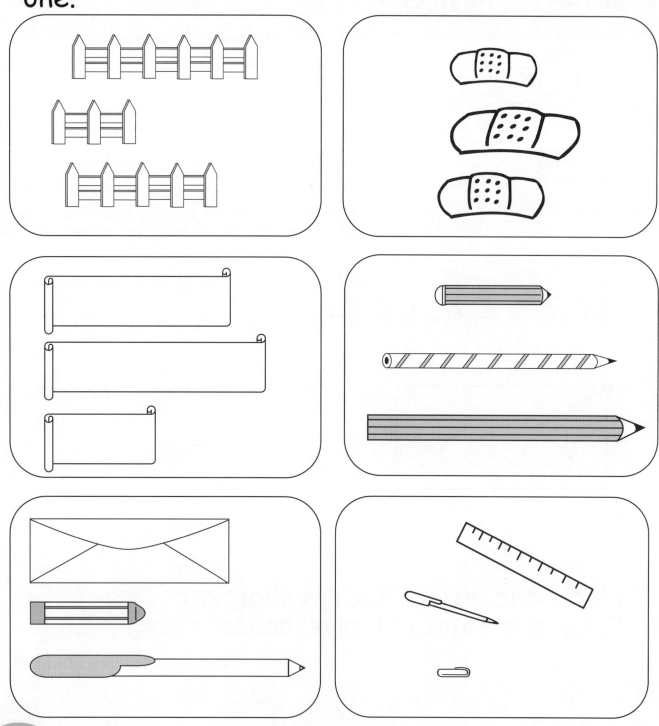

Concept: Compare the length of objects.
Introduction: Draw some thick lines on the board and have children tell you which line is shortest or longest. Use linking cubes or beads that snap together. Ask the child to make different lengths and tell you which one is longest or shortest.

Draw a longer train.

Draw a shorter pencil.

Draw a longer fence.

Concept: Compare the length of objects.
Introduction: Fasten some linking cubes together, or link some paper-clips together. Ask the child to make another one that is shorter or longer than yours.
One Step Further: Encourage the child to point to compare objects around him/her in terms of length.

Unit 10 — Length

Color the longest one red. Color the shortest one yellow.

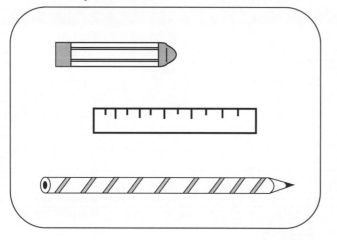

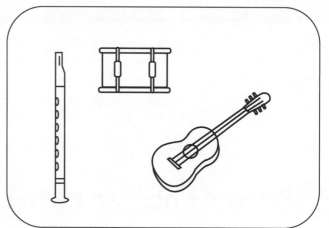

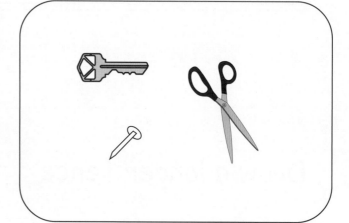

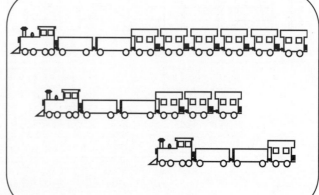

Concept: Compare the length of objects.

Guess, and then measure with paper-clips.

Giraffe	Elephant:
Guess: ___ ⬭ tall	Guess: ___ ⬭ tall
Measure: ___ ⬭ tall	Measure: ___ ⬭ tall

Circle the animal that is taller.
Color the animal that is shorter.

Concept: Compare the height of objects by making direct comparison with reference objects.
Introduction: Name pairs of objects in the room and have the child decide which one is tall and which one is short.

Circle the taller one in each box.

Circle the shorter one in each box.

Concept: Compare the height of objects.
Introduction: Get the child to compare the height of two people. Use the terms 'taller than' and 'shorter than'.

Circle the tallest one. Cross off the shortest one.

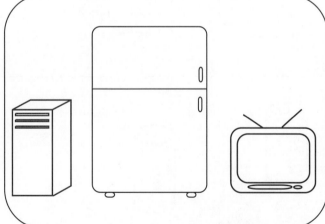

Concept: Compare the height of objects.
Introduction: Name pairs of objects in the room and have the child decide which one is tallest and which one is shortest.

Circle the two that are the same height in each row.

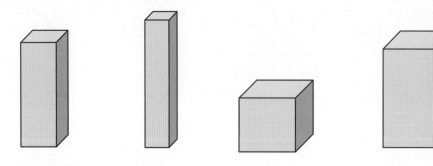

Concept: Compare the height of objects.
Using This Page: This page will be challenging for some children. If the child has difficulty with this page, you can give him/her some linked paper clips to put alongside the objects to find out which two are the same height. By height we are referring to the length of the object, not the height the top is compared to, say, the ground. A child standing at the top of stairs may be 'higher' up than the adult, but the height (length) of the child is not therefore greater than the height of the adult.

Follow the dotted path to help the elephants find their apples.

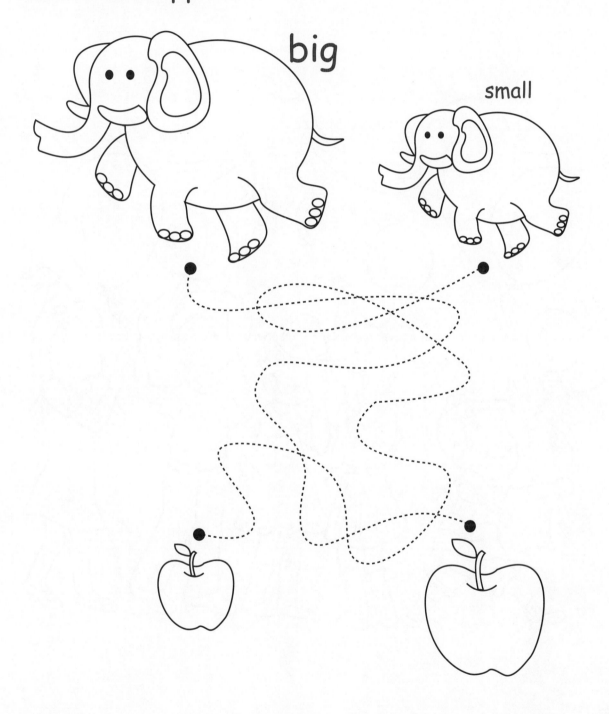

big

small

Concept: Understand the concept of 'big' and 'small'.
Introduction: Display pairs of similar objects such as a big book and a small book, a big block and a small block. Ask the child to pick a pair of similar objects and tell you which one is big and which one is small.
One Step Further: Encourage the child to point to big and small objects around him/her.

Color the big balloons yellow. Color the small balloons red.

Concept: Sort objects by size.
Introduction: Provide a variety of objects that the child can group by size.
One Step Further: Encourage the child to group familiar objects by size.

Which butterfly is smaller? Color it yellow.
Which flower is bigger? Color it red.

Concept: Compare size.
Introduction: Encourage the child to choose between bigger or smaller objects around him/her; e.g., ask the child to "Go sit in the bigger chair."

Draw a bigger moon. Draw some smaller stars. Draw a smaller tree and a bigger tree.

Concept: Compare size.
One Step Further: Have the child draw a picture. Point to something in his/her picture and ask him/her to name another item in the picture that is bigger/smaller.

Draw lines to match the characters to their hats. Color the biggest hat red. Color the smallest hat green. Color the middle-sized hat yellow.

Concept: Compare size.
Introduction: Encourage the child to compare several objects around him/her and decide which is biggest and which is smallest; e.g. ask the child, "Which cushion is the biggest?"

Color the biggest ones. Circle the smallest ones.

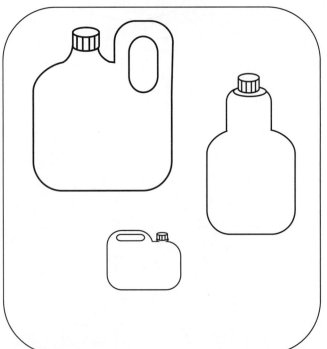

Concept: Compare size.
One Step Further: Discuss ways that growing things get bigger as they grow, not just taller; e.g., a snake does not get much taller as it grows but it gets longer.

Help Little Bear find his things. Circle them.

Concept: Sort by size.
Introduction: Tell the story of <u>Goldilocks and the Three Bears</u>. Use objects as props during the story, such as three sizes of bowls or three sizes of chairs. During the story discuss which bowl or chair should go with which bear and why. After the story, have the child compare the objects according to size.
One Step Further: Let the child wear clothing that are bigger or smaller than his/her own size. Talk about how it feels.

Circle the two that are the same size in each row.

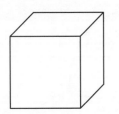   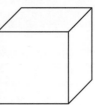 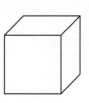

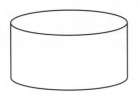 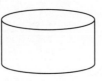

    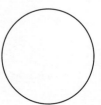

Concept: Estimate size.

Draw something that is heavy.

Draw something that is light.

Concept: Compare weight.
Introduction: Show the child a large light object, such as a balloon, and a small, heavy object, such as a stapler. Get him/her to compare the weights by holding one in each hand. Guide him/her to understand that weight is not necessarily related to size. Have the child decide whether other objects around him/her are heavy or light.

Circle the object that is lighter in each box.

Circle the object that is heavier in each box.

Concept: Compare weight.
Introduction: Put two sets of objects on the table, one with heavier items, and one with lighter items. Ask the child to pick one item from each set and hold one in each hand and compare their weights. Get the child to say, "The _____ is heavier than the _____." and, "The _____ is lighter than the _____." Have the child try to lift objects in the room (such as a chair or a ball) and decide whether the object is heavy, or light, using language such as, "The _____ is heavier than the _____."

Circle the object that is heavier.

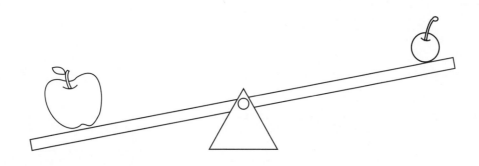

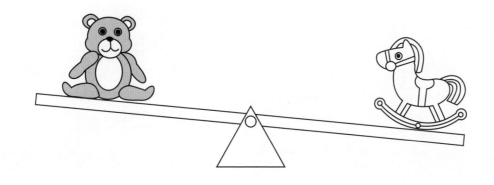

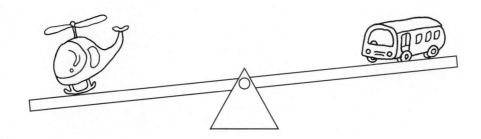

Concept: Compare weight.
Introduction: Provide the child with a simple pan or bucket balance and a variety of objects. Have him/her place two objects on either side of the balance. Get the child to see that the heavier objects make that side of the balance go down farther. Have him/her compare various objects and tell you which one is heavier or lighter.

Circle the item that weighs less.

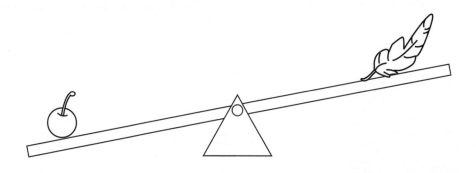

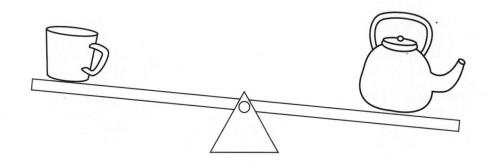

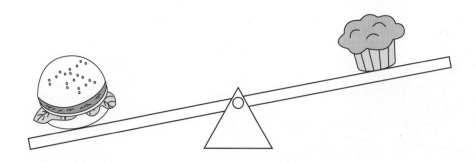

Concept: Compare weight.
Introduction: Have the child compare the weights of objects with a balance. Tell him/her that if one objects is heavier than another, then it weighs more. Ask the child which of the objects **weighs more than** the other or which one **weighs less than** the other.
One Step Further: Have the child see if he/she can find two objects which weigh about the same, i.e. the balance does not tilt. Get him/her to try combinations of objects, e.g. two blocks **weigh the same** as one ball.

The apple is about as heavy as _____ cherries.

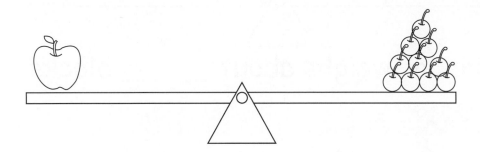

The envelope is about as heavy as _____ paper-clips.

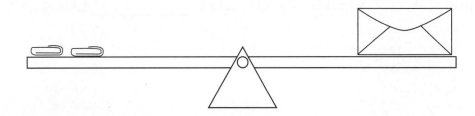

The mug weighs about the same as _____ blocks.

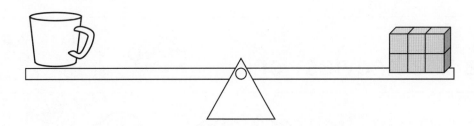

Concept: Compare the weight of objects by making direct comparison to a reference weight.
Introduction: Use a simple pan or bucket balance and some uniform objects, such as blocks or counters, and a selection of objects. Get the child to find out how many blocks weigh about the same as each object. It might not be possible to get the balance to be exactly level. Tell the child that we can say the object weighs about 5 blocks, for example, or a bit less than six blocks.

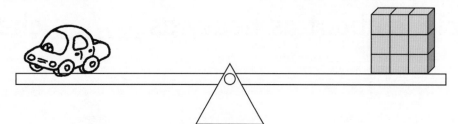

The car weighs about _____ blocks.

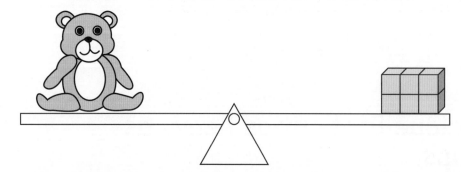

The bear weighs about _____ blocks.

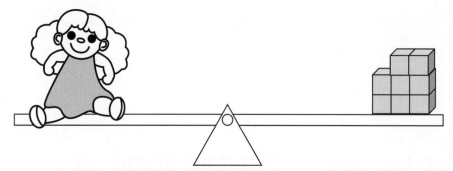

The doll weighs about _____ blocks.

Circle the heaviest one.

Cross out the lightest one.

Concept: Compare the weight of objects by making direct comparison to a reference weight.
Introduction: Have about four objects about the same size and something suitable to weigh them with, such as blocks. Use objects that weigh less than ten blocks. Ask the child to find out how many blocks each object weighs, and then tell you which is heaviest, which is lightest, and which weigh about the same. Then let him/her compare their weights directly. The heaviest objects, for example, should be heavier than all the rest.

Circle the container in each box that can hold more.

Circle the container in each box that can hold less.

Concept: Compare capacity.
Introduction: Provide the child with a bucket of water, or use the sink, and variety of containers. Allow him/her to pour water from one container into another. Select two containers. Ask the child how we can find out which container holds more water. Guide him/her to fill up one container and pour it into the other in order to see which one can hold more water. Have the child use a cup, fill it up, and pour water into a container. Repeat with a different container, perhaps wider. Ask the child if the amount of water changes when it is poured into a different container.

Circle the container in each box that can hold the most.

Circle the container in each box that can hold the least.

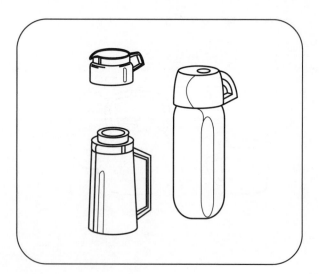

Concept: Compare capacity.
Introduction: Provide the child with a bucket of water, or use the sink, and three containers of similar but not identical capacity. Ask the child to find out which one holds the most, and which one holds the least.

Circle the container that holds more.
Cross out the container that holds less.

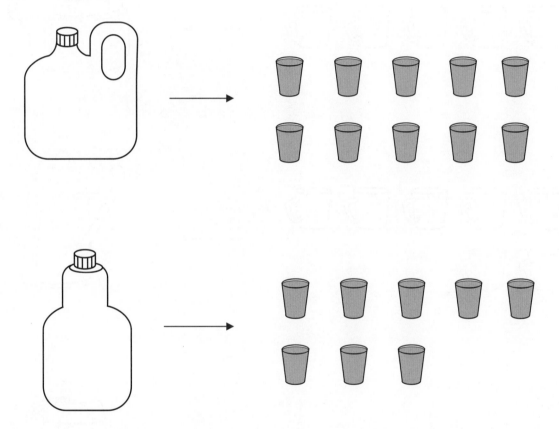

Concept: Compare capacity.
Introduction: Provide some containers that each holds less than 10 cups and some paper cups. Fill the containers with water. Ask the child to pour the water from one container into cups. Line up the cups. Repeat with a second container. Have the child count the cups and tell you which container held more water.
Using This Page: Explain to the child that this page shows how many cups were filled up from the container.

Circle the container that can hold the most. Cross out the container that can hold the least.

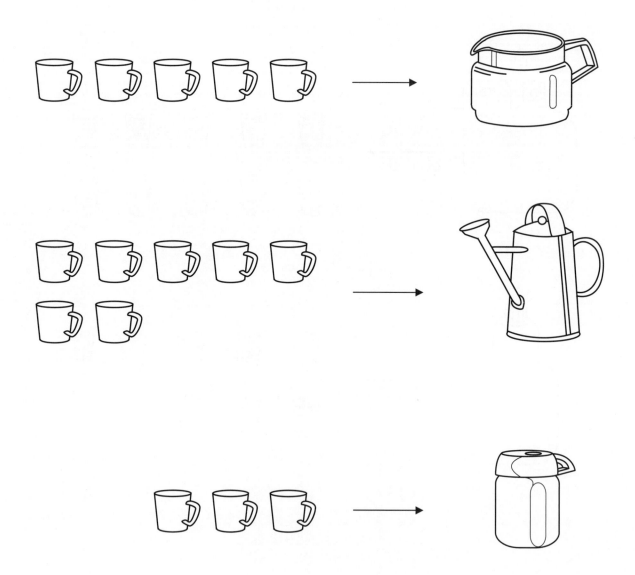

Concept: Compare capacity.
Introduction: Provide the child with a bucket of water, a mug and several containers that hold up to 10 mugs of water. Have the child count how many mugs it takes to fill each container. Help him/her record the number of mugs used. Repeat with the other containers. Them have him/her decide which container holds the most, and which holds the least.
Using This Page: Explain to the children that this page shows how many cups were used to fill up the container.

Draw a line from each apple to each monkey.
Is there an apple for each monkey?

Concept: Recognize equal sets.
Introduction: Demonstrate two sets of objects with the same number in each set, such as three cups and three saucers, or three desks and three chairs. Ask the child questions such as, "Is there a cup for each saucer?" Repeat with other objects.

Draw a line from each rabbit to a carrot. Are there an equal number of rabbits as carrots?

Concept: Recognize equal sets.
Introduction: Provide two sets different objects that can be put together, such as red linking cubes and green linking cubes. Have the same number of objects in each set. Use enough objects that the child can't tell if there is the same number by simply looking at the objects. Have the child pair a red cubes with green cubes to see how the two sets match. Tell the child that the sets are **equal**.

Match each set of children with a set of toys.

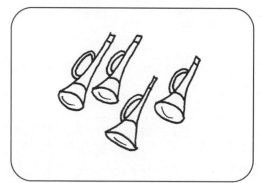

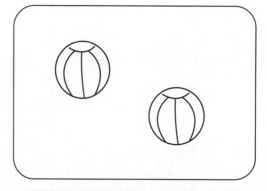

Concept: Match equal sets.
Introduction: Display several sets of one type of object, such as cubes, and several sets of another type of object, such as counters. There should be matching sets of each type. Ask the child to find the pairs of sets that are equal.

Match equal sets.

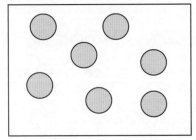

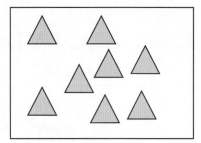

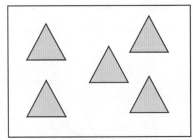

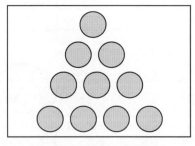

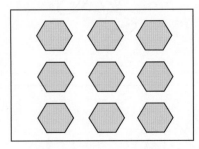

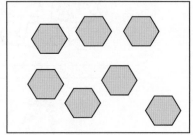

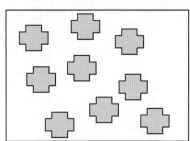

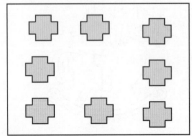

Concept: Match equal sets.
One Step Further: Encourage the child to observe instances when equal sets are made; e.g., setting the table.

Draw a toy for each child.

Concept: Create equal sets.
One Step Further: Use two types of objects. Give the child a set of one type, and ask him/her to create an equal set with the other type.

Draw the same number balloons as there are children.

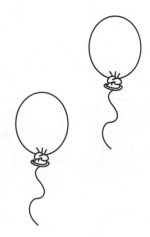

Concept: Create equal sets.

Draw a line from each fisherman to each fish. Are there more fishermen or more fish? Circle the set that has more.

Concept: Compare sets to determine which set has more.
Introduction: Use related objects, such as containers and lids. Place four lids and 6 containers on the table. Ask the child to put a lid on each container. Ask why there are containers without lids. Lead him/her to say that there are **more** containers than lids. Repeat using another set of objects, such as glasses and straws.

Draw a line from each crab to each starfish. Are there more crabs or more starfish? Color the set that has more.

Concept: Compare sets to determine which set has more.
Introduction: Place two sets on the table. Use numbers of items that the child cannot count just by observation, such as a pile of linking cubes and a pile of counters. Ask the child to find out which set has more by matching each item in one set with an item in the other set.

Circle the set in each box that has more.

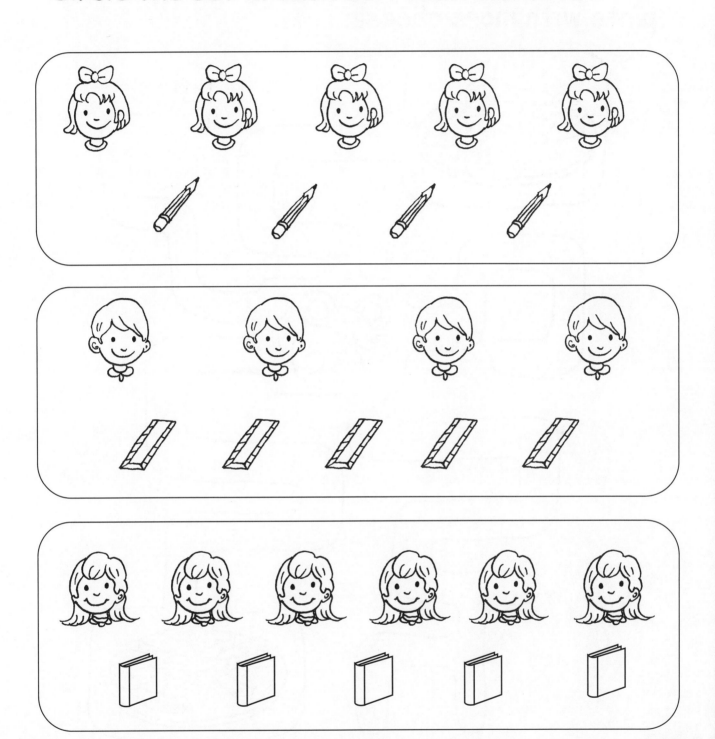

Concept: Compare sets to determine which set has more.
Introduction: Display two sets of 10 or less objects. Ask the child which set has more. Then ask the child to count the number in each set. The set that has more has a larger number.

Follow the path to help the mouse reach the plate with **more** cheese.

Concept: Compare sets to determine which set has more.

Color the set that has more.

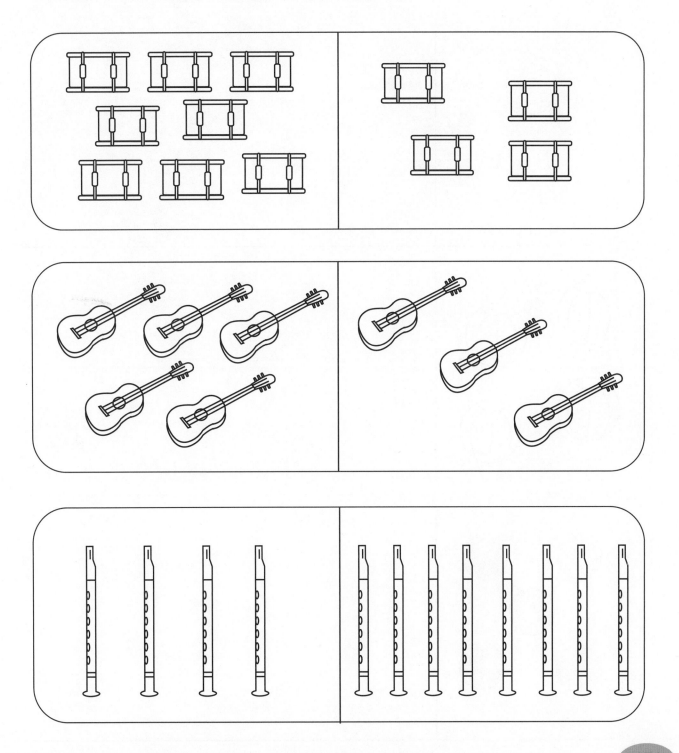

Concept: Compare sets to determine which set has more.
One Step Further: Use two colors of counters. Show the child two handfuls, with one hand holding a set of one color and the other hand holding a set of a different color. Ask the child to guess (estimate) which set has more, and then to match the counters to see if his/her guess was correct.

Draw a set that has more.

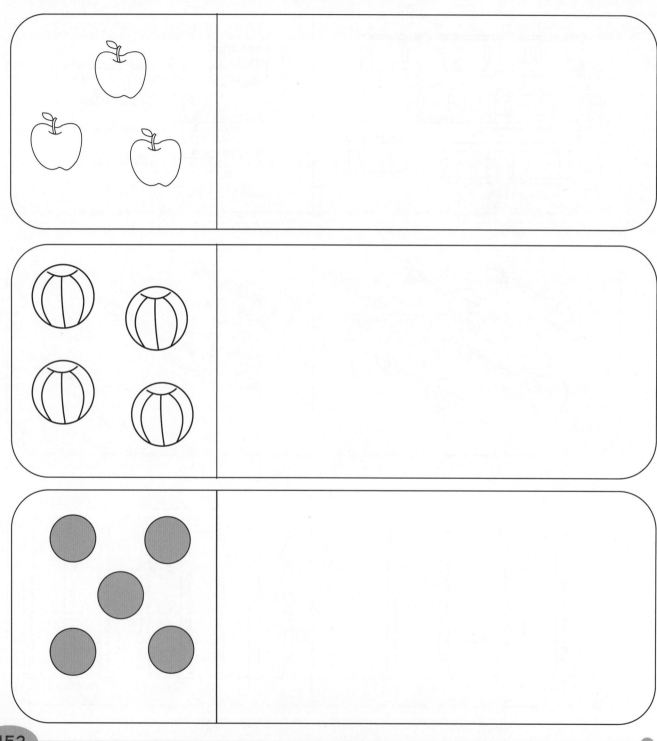

Concept: Create a set that has more.
Introduction: Show a set of objects. Ask the child to create another set that has more.

Draw a line from each butterfly to each flower. Are there less butterflies or less flowers?

Concept: Compare sets to determine which set has less.
Introduction: Show the child two groups of objects of up to five objects with different numbers and ask which set has less. For example, have a set of 5 forks and a set of 4 spoons. Then ask the child to pair a member of one set with a member of the other set. Lead him/her to say that there are **less** spoons than forks. Repeat using another set of objects.

Circle the bird that has less eggs.

Circle the person in each box that has less.

Concept: Compare sets to determine which set has less.
Introduction: Draw two sets of objects on the board. Have the child draw lines from each item in one set to each item in the other set and tell you which set has less.

Match the animals with one food item each. Circle the set that has less.

Concept: Compare sets to determine which set has less.
Introduction: Display two sets of 10 or less objects. Ask the child which set has less. Then ask the child to count the number in each set. The set that has less has a smaller number.

Color the set of balloons that has less.

 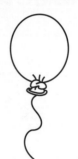

Color the birthday cake that has less candles.

Color the ladybug that has less spots.

Concept: Compare sets to determine which set has less.

Less

Color the set that has less.

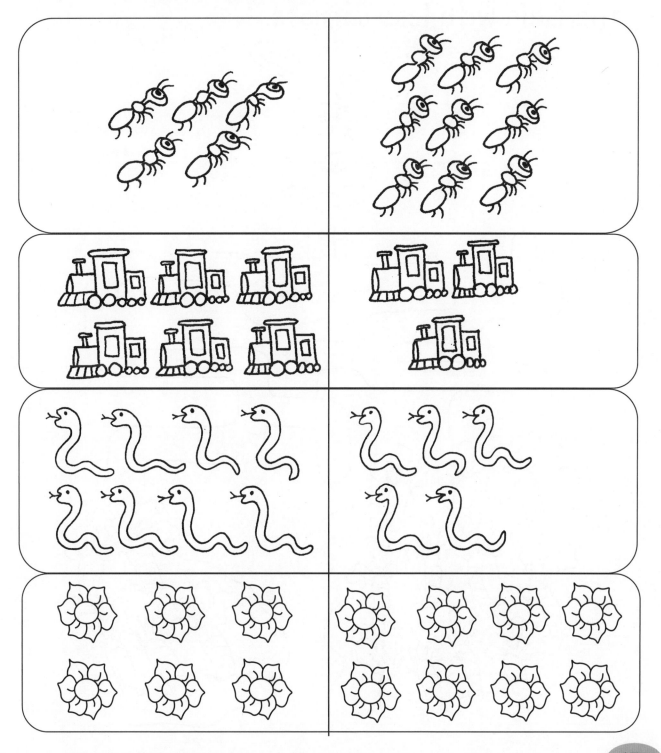

Concept: Compare sets to determine which set has less.
Introduction: Display two sets of blocks, arranged in columns and rows, one with one less column or row than the other. Ask a child which set has less. Ask him/her to point out why he/she thinks that set has less.

Follow the path to help the rabbit to find the field with **less** carrots.

Concept: Compare sets to determine which set has less.